COLLECT BRITISH STAMPS

A STANLEY GIBBONS CHECKLIST OF
THE STAMPS OF GREAT BRITAIN

1998 (Forty-ninth) Edition

STANLEY GIBBONS LTD

By Appointment to H. M. the Queen
Stanley Gibbons Ltd, London Philatelists.

London and Ringwood

COLLECT BRITISH STAMPS

The 1998 Edition

From the famous Penny Black of 1840 to the absorbing issues of today, the stamps of Great Britain are highly popular with collectors. *Collect British Stamps* has been our message since very early days – but particularly since the First Edition of this checklist in September 1967. This 49th edition includes all the recent issues. Prices have been carefully revised to reflect today's market. Total sales of *Collect British Stamps* are now over $3\frac{1}{2}$ million copies.

Collect British Stamps appears in the autumn of each year. A more detailed Great Britain catalogue, the *Concise*, is published each spring. The *Great Britain Concise* incorporates many additional listings covering watermark varieties, phosphor omitted errors, missing colour errors, stamp booklets and special commemorative First Day Cover postmarks. It is ideally suited for the collector who wishes to discover more about GB stamps.

Listings in this edition of *Collect British Stamps* include all 1997 issues which have appeared up to the publication date.

Scope. *Collect British Stamps* comprises:
- All stamps with different watermark (*wmk*) or perforation (*perf*).
- Visible plate numbers on the Victorian issues.
- Graphite-lined and phosphor issues, including variations in the number of phosphor bands.
- First Day Covers for Definitives from 1952, Regionals and all Special Issues.
- Presentation, Gift and Souvenir Packs.
- Post Office Yearbooks.
- Regional issues and War Occupation stamps of Guernsey and Jersey.
- Postage Due and Official Stamps.
- Post Office Picture Cards (PHQ cards).
- Commemorative gutter pairs and "Traffic Light" gutter pairs listed as mint sets.
- Royal Mail Postage Labels priced as sets and on P.O. First Day Cover.

Stamps of the independent postal administrations of Guernsey, Isle of Man and Jersey are contained in *Collect Channel Islands and Isle of Man Stamps*.

Layout. Stamps are set out chronologically by date of issue. In the catalogue lists the first numeral is the Stanley Gibbons catalogue number; the black (boldface) numeral alongside is the type number referring to the respective illustration. A blank in this column implies that the number immediately above is repeated. The denomination and colour of the stamp are then shown. Before February 1971 British currency was:

   £1 = 20s   One pound = twenty shillings *and*
   1s = 12d   One shilling = twelve pence.

Upon decimalisation this became:

   £1 = 100p   One pound = one hundred (new) pence.

The catalogue list then shows two price columns. The left-hand is for unused stamps and the right-hand for used. Corresponding small boxes are provided in which collectors may wish to check off the items in their collection.

Our method of indicating prices is:
Numerals for pence, e.g. 10 denotes 10p (10 pence). Numerals for pounds and pence, e.g. 4·25 denotes £4·25 (4 pounds and 25 pence). For £100 and above, prices are in whole pounds and so include the £ sign and omit the zeros for pence.

Colour illustrations. The colour illustrations of stamps are intended as a guide only; they may differ in shade from the originals.

Size of illustrations. To comply with Post Office regulations stamp illustrations are three-quarters linear size. Separate illustrations of surcharges, overprints and watermarks are actual size.

Prices. Prices quoted in this catalogue are our selling prices at the time the book went to press. They are for stamps in fine condition; in issues where condition varies we may ask more for the

superb and less for the sub-standard. The unused prices for stamps of Queen Victoria to King Edward VIII are for lightly hinged examples. Unused prices for King George VI and Queen Elizabeth II are for unmounted mint (though when not available unmounted, mounted stamps are often supplied at a lower price). Prices for used stamps refer to postally used copies. All prices are subject to change without prior notice and we give no guarantee to supply all stamps priced, since it is not possible to keep every catalogued item in stock. Individual low value stamps sold at 399, Strand are liable to an additional handling charge. Commemorative issues may, at times, only be available in complete sets.

In the price columns:

† = Does not exist.

(—) or blank = Exists, or may exist, but price cannot be quoted.

* = Not normally issued (the so-called 'Abnormals' of 1862–80).

Perforations. The 'perforation' is the number of holes in a length of 2 cm, as measured by the Gibbons *Instanta* gauge. The stamp is viewed against a dark background with the transparent gauge put on top of it. Perforations are quoted to the nearest half. Stamps without perforation are termed 'imperforate'.

From 1992 certain stamps occur with a large elliptical (oval) hole inserted in each line of vertical perforations. The £10 definitive, No. 1658, is unique in having two such holes in the horizontal perforations.

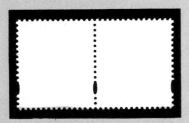

Elliptical perforations

Se-tenant combinations. *Se-tenant* means 'joined together'. Some sets include stamps of different design arranged *se-tenant* as blocks or strips and these are often collected unsevered as issued. Where such combinations exist the stamps are priced both mint and used, as singles or complete combinations. The set price for mint refers to the unsevered combination plus singles of any other values in the set. The used set price is for single stamps of all values.

First day covers. Prices for first day covers are for complete sets used on plain covers (1924, 1925, 1929) or on special covers (1935 onwards), the stamps of which are cancelled with ordinary operational postmarks (1924–1962) or by the *standard* "First Day of Issue" postmarks (1963 onwards). The British Post Office did not provide "First Day" treatment for every definitive issued after 1963. Where the stamps in a set were issued on different days, prices are for a cover from each day.

Presentation Packs. Special packs comprising slip-in cards with printed information inside a protective covering, were introduced for the 1964 Shakespeare issue. Collectors packs, containing commemoratives from the preceding twelve months, were issued from 1967. Some packs with text in German from 1968–69 exist as does a Japanese version of the pack for Nos. 916/17. Yearbooks, hardbound and illustrated in colour within a slip cover, joined the product range in 1984.

PHQ cards. Since 1973 the Post Office has produced a series of picture cards, which can be sent through the post as postcards. Each card shows an enlarged colour reproduction of a current British stamp, either of one or more values from a set or of all values. Cards are priced here in fine mint condition for sets complete as issued. The Post Office gives each card a 'PHQ' serial number, hence the term. The cards are usually on sale shortly before the date of issue of the stamps, but there is no officially designated 'first day'.

Used prices are for cards franked with the stamp depicted, on the obverse or reverse, the stamp being cancelled with an official postmark for first day of issue.

Gutter pairs. All modern Great Britain commemoratives are produced in sheets containing two panes of stamps separated by a blank horizontal or vertical margin known as a gutter. This feature first made its appearance on some supplies of the 1972 Royal Silver Wedding 3p, and marked the introduction of Harrison & Sons' new "Jumelle" stamp-printing press. There are advantages for both the printer and the Post Office in such a layout which has now been used for all commemorative issues since 1974.

The term "gutter pair" is used for a pair of stamps separated by part of the blank gutter margin.

Traffic light gutter pair

Gutter pair

Most printers include some form of colour check device on the sheet margins, in addition to the cylinder or plate numbers. Harrison & Sons use round "dabs", or spots of colour, resembling traffic lights. For the period from the 1972 Royal Silver Wedding until the end of 1979 these colour dabs appeared in the gutter margin. Gutter pairs showing these "traffic lights" are worth considerably more than the normal version.

Catalogue numbers used. The checklist uses the same catalogue numbers as the Stanley Gibbons *British Commonwealth* Catalogue (Part 1), 1998 edition.

Latest issue date for stamps recorded in this edition is 13 November 1997.

STANLEY GIBBONS LTD

Head Office: 399 Strand, London WC2R 0LX.

Auction Room and Specialist Stamp Departments—Open Monday-Friday 9.30 a.m. to 5 p.m.

Shop—Open Monday to Friday 8.30 a.m. to 6 p.m. and Saturday 10.00 a.m. to 4 p.m.

Telephone 0171-836 8444 for all departments

Stanley Gibbons Publications:
5, Parkside, Christchurch Road, Ringwood, Hants BH24 3SH.
Telephone 01425 472363
Publications Mail Order
FREEPHONE 0800 611622
Trade Desk 01425 478776

ISBN: 0-85259-433-X
© Stanley Gibbons Ltd 1997

QUEEN VICTORIA

1837 (20 June)–1901 (22 Jan.)

IDENTIFICATION. In this checklist Victorian stamps are classified firstly according to which printing method was used – line-engraving, embossing or surface-printing.

Corner letters. Numerous stamps also have letters in all four, or just the lower, corners. These were an anti-forgery device and the letters differ from stamp to stamp. If present in all four corners the upper pair are the reverse of the lower. Note the importance of these corner letters in the way the checklist is arranged.

Watermarks. Further classification depends on watermarks: these are illustrated in normal position, with stamps priced accordingly.

1 Line-engraved Issues

1

1a

2

2a White lines added above and below head

3 Small Crown watermark

4 Large Crown watermark

Letters in lower corners

1840 *Wmk Small Crown Type 3* *Imperforate*

Cat. No.	Type		Unused	Used		
2	1	1d black	£3000	£150	□	□
5	2	2d blue	£5500	£325	□	□

1841

8	1a	1d red-brown	£130	5·00	□	□
14	2a	2d blue	£1000	48.00	□	□

1854–57 (*i*) *Wmk Small Crown Type 3* *Perf 16*

17	1a	1d red-brown	£140	6·00	□	□
19	2a	2d blue	£1500	45·00	□	□

(*ii*) *Wmk Small Crown Type 3* *Perf 14*

24	1a	1d red-brown	£275	22·00	□	□
23	2a	2d blue	£2000	£125	□	□

(*iii*) *Wmk Large Crown Type 4* *Perf 16*

26	1a	1d red	£550	40·00	□	□
27	2a	2d blue	£2500	£150	□	□

(*iv*) *Wmk Large Crown Type 4* *Perf 14*

40	1a	1d red	25·00	3·00	□	□
34	2a	2d blue	£1200	35·00	□	□

5

6 Watermark extending over three stamps

7

8

9

Letters in all four corners

Plate numbers. Stamps included a 'plate number' in their design and this affects valuation. The cheapest plates are priced here; see complete list of plate numbers overleaf.

1858–70 (*i*) *Wmk Type 6* *Perf 14*

48	5	½d red	50·00	10·00	□	□

(*ii*) *Wmk Large Crown Type 4* *Perf 14*

43	7	1d red	5·00	1·50	□	□
51	8	1½d red	£200	28·00	□	□
45	9	2d blue	£150	5·50	□	□

PLATE NUMBERS
on stamps of 1858–70 having letters in all four corners

Positions of Plate Numbers

Shows
Plate 9 (½d)

Shows
Plate 170 (1d 2d)

Shows
Plate 3 (1½d)

HALFPENNY VALUE (S.G. 48)

Plate	Un.	Used			Plate	Un.	Used		
1	£100	50·00	L	L	11	50·00	10·00	L	L
3	60·00	18·00	L	L	12	50·00	10·00	L	L
4	75·00	12·00			13	50·00	10·00		
5	55·00	10·00	L	L	14	50·00	10·00	L	L
6	50·00	10·00	L	L	15	60·00	15·00	L	L
8	£100	55·00	L	L	19	95·00	28·00	□	□
9	£2250	£350	L	L	20	£100	40·00	□	□
10	75·00	10·00							

Plates 2, 7, 16, 17 and 18 were not completed, while Plates 21 and 22 though made, were not used. Plate 9 was a reserve plate, not greatly used

PENNY VALUE (S.G. 43)

Plate	Un.	Used			Plate	Un.	Used			Plate	Un.	Used			Plate	Un.	Used		
71	15·00	2·00	□	□	112	32·00	1·50	□	□	154	10·00	1·00	□	□	190	10·00	3·50	□	□
72	20·00	2·50	□	□	113	10·00	7·50	□	□	155	10·00	1·50	□	□	191	5·00	4·00	□	□
73	15·00	2·00	□	□	114	£190	8·00	□	□	156	10·00	1·00	□	□	192	15·00	1·00	□	□
74	12·00	1·00	□	□	115	55·00	1·50	□	□	157	10·00	1·00	□	□	193	5·00	1·00	□	□
76	22·00	1·00	□	□	116	40·00	6·00	□	□	158	5·00	1·00	□	□	194	10·00	5·00	□	□
77	£100 000	£80 000	□	□	117	10·00	1·00	□	□	159	5·00	1·00	□	□	195	10·00	5·00	□	□
78	55·00	1·00	□	□	118	15·00	1·00	□	□	160	5·00	1·00	□	□	196	8·00	3·00	□	□
79	18·00	1·00	□	□	119	8·00	1·00	□	□	161	18·00	4·00	□	□	197	10·00	6·00	□	□
80	12·00	1·00	□	□	120	5·00	1·00	□	□	162	10·00	4·00	□	□	198	6·00	3·50	□	□
81	32·00	1·50	□	□	121	22·00	6·00	□	□	163	10·00	2·00	□	□	199	12·00	3·50	□	□
82	65·00	2·50	□	□	122	5·00	1·00	□	□	164	10·00	2·00	□	□	200	12·00	1·00	□	□
83	80·00	4·00	□	□	123	8·00	1·00	□	□	165	12·00	1·00	□	□	201	5·00	3·00	□	□
84	32·00	1·50	□	□	124	8·00	1·00	□	□	166	10·00	3·50	□	□	202	10·00	5·00	□	□
85	15·00	1·50	□	□	125	8·00	1·50	□	□	167	8·00	1·00	□	□	203	5·00	10·00	□	□
86	18·00	2·50	□	□	127	20·00	1·50	□	□	168	8·00	5·50	□	□	204	8·00	1·50	□	□
87	5·00	1·00	□	□	129	8·00	5·00	□	□	169	18·00	4·00	□	□	205	8·00	2·00	□	□
88	90·00	5·50	□	□	130	12·00	1·50	□	□	170	8·00	1·00	□	□	206	8·00	6·00	□	□
89	22·00	1·00	□	□	131	40·00	11·00	□	□	171	5·00	1·00	□	□	207	8·00	6·00	□	□
90	16·00	1·00	□	□	132	55·00	16·00	□	□	172	5·00	1·00	□	□	208	8·00	10·00	□	□
91	22·00	3·50	□	□	133	50·00	6·00	□	□	173	28·00	6·00	□	□	209	10·00	6·00	□	□
92	10·00	1·00	□	□	134	5·00	1·00	□	□	174	5·00	1·00	□	□	210	12·00	8·00	□	□
93	22·00	1·00	□	□	135	55·00	20·00	□	□	175	20·00	2·00	□	□	211	25·00	15·00	□	□
94	22·00	3·00	□	□	136	55·00	15·00	□	□	176	15·00	1·50	□	□	212	10·00	7·50	□	□
95	15·00	1·00	□	□	137	10·00	1·50	□	□	177	8·00	1·00	□	□	213	10·00	7·50	□	□
96	16·00	1·00	□	□	138	8·00	1·00	□	□	178	10·00	2·00	□	□	214	15·00	13·00	□	□
97	10·00	2·00	□	□	139	18·00	11·00	□	□	179	10·00	1·50	□	□	215	15·00	13·00	□	□
98	10·00	3·50	□	□	140	8·00	1·00	□	□	180	10·00	3·00	□	□	216	15·00	13·00	□	□
99	15·00	3·00	□	L	141	80·00	6·00	□	□	181	10·00	1·00	□	□	217	12·00	4·00	□	□
100	20·00	1·50	□	□	142	28·00	18·00	□	□	182	55·00	3·00	□	□	218	8·00	5·00	□	□
101	28·00	6·00	□	□	143	18·00	10·00	□	□	183	15·00	2·00	□	□	219	32·00	50·00	□	□
102	12·00	1·00	□	□	144	55·00	15·00	□	□	184	5·00	1·50	□	□	220	5·00	4·00	□	□
103	12·00	2·00	□	□	145	5·00	1·50	□	□	185	10·00	2·00	□	□	221	18·00	10·00	□	□
104	16·00	3·00	□	□	146	8·00	3·50	□	□	186	18·00	1·50	□	□	222	28·00	25·00	□	□
105	38·00	4·00	□	□	147	12·00	2·00	□	□	187	8·00	1·00	□	□	223	32·00	40·00	□	□
106	18·00	1·00	□	□	148	12·00	2·00	□	□	188	12·00	7·00	□	□	224	38·00	35·00	□	□
107	22·00	3·75	□	□	149	10·00	3·50	□	□	189	20·00	4·00	□	□	225	£1100	£350	□	□
108	18·00	1·50	□	□	150	5·00	1·00	□	□										
109	40·00	2·00	□	□	151	15·00	6·00	□	□										
110	12·00	6·00	□	□	152	12·00	3·25	□	□										
111	20·00	1·50	□	□	153	40·00	6·00	□	□										

Plates 69, 70, 75, 77, 126 and 128 were prepared but rejected. No stamps therefore exist, except for a very few from Plate 77 which somehow reached the public. Plate 177 stamps, by accident or design, are sometimes passed off as the rare Plate 77

THREE-HALFPENNY VALUE (S.G. 51)

Plate	Un.	Used			Plate	Un.	Used		
(1)	£400	45·00	L	L	3	£200	28·00	L	L

Plate 1 did *not* have the plate number in the design. Plate 2 was not completed and no stamps exist

TWOPENNY VALUE (S.G. 45)

Plate	Un.	Used			Plate	Un.	Used		
7	£400	20·00	□	□	13	£180	10·00	□	□
8	£450	15·00	□	□	14	£200	12·00	□	□
9	£150	5·50	□	□	15	£160	10·00	□	□
12	£750	45·00	□	□					

Plates 10 and 11 were prepared but rejected

2 Embossed Issues

Prices are for stamps cut square and with average to fine embossing. Stamps with exceptionally clear embossing are worth more.

10　　　　　　11　　　　　　12

13

1847–54 Wmk 13 (6d), no wmk (others)		Imperforate			
59	10	6d lilac	£3000	£475	☐ ☐
57	11	10d brown	£2750	£650	☐ ☐
64	12	1s green	£3250	£425	☐ ☐

3 Surface-printed Issues

IDENTIFICATION. Check first whether the design includes corner letters or not, as mentioned for 'Line-engraved issues'. The checklist is divided up according to whether any letters are small or large, also whether they are white (uncoloured) or printed in the colour of the stamp. Further identification then depends on watermark.

PERFORATION. Except for Nos. 126/9 all the following issues of Queen Victoria are perf 14.

14

15 Small Garter　16 Medium Garter　17 Large Garter

18　　　　　　19　　　　　　20 Emblems

No corner letters

1855–57 (i) Wmk Small Garter Type 15					
62	14	4d red	£2500	£200	☐ ☐
(ii) Wmk Medium Garter Type 16					
64	14	4d red	£2000	£180	☐ ☐
(iii) Wmk Large Garter Type 17					
66a	14	4d red	£650	40·00	☐ ☐
(iv) Wmk Emblems Type 20					
70	18	6d lilac	£525	50·00	☐ ☐
72	19	1s green	£675	£150	☐ ☐

Plate numbers. Stamps Nos. 90/163 should be checked for the 'plate numbers' indicated, as this affects valuation (the cheapest plates are priced here). The mark 'Pl.' shows that several numbers exist, priced in a separate list overleaf.

Plate numbers are the small numerals appearing in duplicate in some part of the frame design or adjacent to the lower corner letters (in the 5s value a single numeral above the lower inscription).

21　　　　　　22　　　　　　23

24　　　　　　　　25

Small white corner letters

1862–64 Wmk Emblems Type 20, except 4d (Large Garter Type 17)					
76	21	3d red	£750	£120	☐ ☐
80	22	4d red	£550	40·00	☐ ☐
84	23	6d lilac	£675	40·00	☐ ☐
87	24	9d bistre	£1400	£150	☐ ☐
90	25	1s green Pl.	£800	80·00	☐ ☐

3

26

27

28 (hyphen in SIX-PENCE)

32

33 Spray of Rose

34

29

30

31

Large white corner letters

1865–67 *Wmk Emblems Type* **20**. *except* 4d (*Large Garter Type* **17**)

92	**26**	3d red (Plate 4) ..	£450	50·00 □ □
94	**27**	4d vermilion *Pl.* ..	£250	25·00 □ □
97	**28**	6d lilac *Pl.*	£375	40·00 □ □
98	**29**	9d straw *Pl.*	£800	£250 □ □
99	**30**	10d brown (Plate 1)	†£13000	□
101	**31**	1s green (Plate 4)	£725	80·00 □ □

1867–80 *Wmk Spray of Rose Type* **33**

103	**26**	3d red *Pl.*	£250	16·00 □ □
105	**28**	6d lilac (with hyphen) (Plate 6)	£600	40·00 □ □
109		6d mauve (without hyphen) *Pl.* ..	£300	35·00 □ □
110	**29**	9d straw (Plate 4)	£675	£120 □ □
112	**30**	10d brown *Pl.*	£1100	£190 □ □
117	**31**	1s green *Pl.*	£375	15·00 □ □
119	**32**	2s blue *Pl.*	£1100	75·00 □ □
121		2s brown (Plate 1)	£7500	£1500 □ □

1872–73 *Wmk Spray of Rose Type* **33**

122b	**34**	6d brown *Pl.*	£375	25·00 □ □
125		6d grey (Plate 12)	£800	£130 □ □

PLATE NUMBERS
on stamps
of 1862–83

Cat No		Plate No	Un	Used		

Small White Corner Letters (1862–64)

90	1s green	2	£800	80·00 □ □
		3	£12000		□ □

Plate 2 is actually numbered as '1' and Plate 3 as '2' on the stamps.

Large White Corner Letters (1865–83)

103	3d red	4	£350	70·00 □ □
		5	£250	18·00 □ □
		6	£275	16·00 □ □
		7	£350	20·00 □ □
		8	£300	18·00 □ □
		9	£300	25·00 □ □
		10	£350	55·00 □ □
94	4d verm	7	£325	28·00 □ □
		8	£275	28·00 □ □
		9	£275	25·00 □ □
		10	£325	40·00 □ □
		11	£275	25·00 □ □
		12	£250	25·00 □ □
		13	£275	25·00 □ □
		14	£325	50·00 □ □
97	6d lilac	5	£375	40·00 □ □
		6	£1100	70·00 □ □
109	6d mauve	8	£300	35·00 □ □
		9	£300	35·00 □ □
		10	·	£13000 □ □
122b	6d brown	11	£375	25·00 □ □
		12	£850	80·00 □ □

98	9d straw	4	£800	£250 □ □
		5	£10000	□ □
112	10d brown	1	£1100	£190 □ □
		2	£13000	£2750 □ □
117	1s green	4	£375	20·00 □ □
		5	£425	18·00 □ □
		6	£600	15·00 □ □
		7	£600	40·00 □ □
119	2s blue	1	£1100	75·00 □ □
		3		£3250 □ □
126	5s red	1	£3000	£350 □ □
		2	£4000	£400 □ □

Large Coloured Corner Letters (1873–83)

139	2½d mauve	1	£275	45·00 □ □
		2	£275	45·00 □ □
		3	£450	50·00 □ □
141	2½d mauve	3	£600	50·00 □ □
		4	£250	20·00 □ □
		5	£250	25·00 □ □
		6	£250	20·00 □ □
		7	£250	20·00 □ □
		8	£250	25·00 □ □
		9	£250	20·00 □ □
		10	£300	35·00 □ □
		11	£250	20·00 □ □
		12	£250	25·00 □ □
		13	£250	25·00 □ □
		14	£250	20·00 □ □
		15	£250	20·00 □ □
		16	£250	20·00 □ □
		17	£650	£130 □ □
142	2½d blue	17	£225	28·00 □ □
		18	£250	20·00 □ □
		19	£225	18·00 □ □
		20	£225	18·00 □ □

157	2½d blue	21	£250	15·00 □ □
		22	£200	15·00 □ □
		23	£200	10·00 □ □
143	3d red	11	£225	18·00 □ □
		12	£250	18·00 □ □
		14	£275	20·00 □ □
		15	£225	18·00 □ □
		16	£225	18·00 □ □
		17	£250	18·00 □ □
		18	£250	18·00 □ □
		19	£225	18·00 □ □
		20	£225	38·00 □ □
158	3d red	20	£300	55·00 □ □
		21	£275	45·00 □ □
152	4d verm	15	£750	£170 □ □
		16	·	£11000 □ □
153	4d green	15	£550	£140 □ □
		16	£475	£120 □ □
		17	·	£6500 □ □
160	4d brown	17	£200	30·00 □ □
		18	£200	30·00 □ □
147	6d grey	13	£250	28·00 □ □
		14	£250	28·00 □ □
		15	£250	25·00 □ □
		16	£250	25·00 □ □
		17	£350	50·00 □ □
161	6d grey	17	£200	32·00 □ □
		18	£190	32·00 □ □
150	1s green	8	£375	50·00 □ □
		9	£375	50·00 □ □
		10	£350	50·00 □ □
		11	£350	50·00 □ □
		12	£300	35·00 □ □
		13	£300	35·00 □ □
		14	·	£11000 □ □
163	1s brown	13	£325	75·00 □ □
		14	£275	75·00 □ □

35

36

37

38

44

45

46

47 Small Anchor   **48** Orb

Large coloured corner letters

1873–80 (*i*) *Wmk Small Anchor Type* **47**

139	**41**	2½d mauve *Pl.*	£275	45·00	☐ ☐

(*ii*) *Wmk Orb Type* **48**

| 141 | **41** | 2½d mauve *Pl.* | £250 | 20·00 | ☐ ☐ |
| 142 | | 2½d blue *Pl.* | £225 | 18·00 | ☐ ☐ |

(*iii*) *Wmk Spray of Rose Type* **33**

143	**42**	3d red *Pl.*	£225	18·00	☐ ☐
145	**43**	6d pale buff (Plate 13)	·	£5000	☐ ☐
147		6d grey *Pl.*	£250	25·00	☐ ☐
150	**44**	1s green *Pl.*	£300	35·00	☐ ☐
151		1s brown (Plate 13)	£1300	£250	☐ ☐

(*iv*) *Wmk Large Garter Type* **17**

152	**45**	4d vermilion *Pl.*	£750	£170	☐ ☐
153		4d green *Pl.*	£475	£120	☐ ☐
154		4d brown (Plate 17)	£700	£200	☐ ☐
156	**46**	8d orange (Plate 1)	£600	£175	☐ ☐

49 Imperial Crown   (**50**) Surcharges in red (**51**)

1880–83 *Wmk Imperial Crown Type* **49**

157	**41**	2½d blue *Pl.*	£200	10·00	☐ ☐
158	**42**	3d red *Pl.*	£275	45·00	☐ ☐
159		3d on 3d lilac (surch Type **50**)	£250	80·00	☐ ☐
160	**45**	4d brown *Pl.*	£200	30·00	☐ ☐
161	**43**	6d grey *Pl.*	£190	32·00	☐ ☐
162		6d on 6d lilac (surch Type **51**)	£225	80·00	☐ ☐
163	**44**	1s brown *Pl.*	£275	75·00	☐ ☐

39 Maltese Cross   **40** Large Anchor

1867–83 (*i*) *Wmk Maltese Cross Type* **39**   *Perf* 15½ × 15

126	**35**	5s red *Pl.*	£3000	£350	☐ ☐
128	**36**	10s grey (Plate 1)	£21000	£1000	☐ ☐
129	**37**	£1 brown (Plate 1)	£26000	£1600	☐ ☐

(*ii*) *Wmk Large Anchor Type* **40**   *Perf* 14

134	**35**	5s red (Plate 4)	£5500	£1100	☐ ☐
131	**36**	10s grey (Plate 1)	£24000	£1600	☐ ☐
132	**37**	£1 brown (Plate 1)	£30000	£2750	☐ ☐
137	**38**	£5 orange (Plate 1)	£5000	£1600	☐ ☐

41   42   43

52

53

54

55

56

1880—81 *Wmk Imperial Crown Type* **49**

164	**52**	½d green	..	20·00	5·00	□	□
166	**53**	1d brown	..	8·00	5·00	□	□
167	**54**	1½d brown	..	95·00	20·00	□	□
168	**55**	2d red	..	£110	45·00	□	□
169	**56**	5d indigo	..	£375	60·00	□	□

57

Die I

Die II

1881 *Wmk Imperial Crown Type* **49**

(*a*) 14 *dots in each corner, Die* I

171	**57**	1d lilac		80·00	15·00	□	□

(*b*) 16 *dots in each corner, Die* II

173	**57**	1d lilac	..	1·50	75	□	□

58

59

60

Coloured letters in the corners

1883-84 *Wmk Anchor Type* **40**

179	**58**	2s 6d deep lilac	..	£250	70·00	□	□
181	**59**	5s red	.. ..	£450	90·00	□	□
183	**60**	10s blue	.. ..	£850	£275	□	□

61

1884 *Wmk* 3 *Imperial Crowns Type* **49**

185	**61**	£1 brown	..	£12000	£1000	□ □

1888 *Wmk* 3 *Orbs Type* **48**

186	**61**	£1 brown	..	£18000	£1500	□ □

1891 *Wmk* 3 *Imperial Crowns Type* **49**

212	**61**	£1 green	..	£2250	£400	□ □

62

63

64

65

66

1883—84 *Wmk Imperial Crown Type* **49** (*sideways on horiz designs*)

187	**52**	½d blue	.. ..	12·00	3·00	□	□
188	**62**	1½d lilac	.. .. ..	65·00	22·00	□	□
189	**63**	2d lilac	.. .. ..	95·00	45·00	□	□
190	**64**	2½d lilac	.. .. ..	50·00	8·00	□	□
191	**65**	3d lilac	.. .. ..	£125	65·00	□	□
192	**66**	4d dull green	.. ..	£325	£130	□	□
193	**62**	5d dull green	.. ..	£325	£130	□	□
194	**63**	6d dull green	.. ..	£350	£140	□	□
195	**64**	9d dull green	.. ..	£650	£325	□	□
196	**65**	1s dull green	.. ..	£450	£175	□	□

The above prices are for stamps in the true dull green colour. Stamps which have been soaked, causing the colour to run, are virtually worthless.

67
 68
 69

 70
 71
 72

 73
 74
 75

 76 **77** **78**

 79
 80 **81**

 82 **83** **84**

 85 **86** **87**

 88 **89**

 **90**
 91
 92

 **93**

'Jubilee' issue

1887–1900 *The bicoloured stamps have the value tablets,*
or the frames including the value tablets, in the second colour.
Wmk Imperial Crown Type 49

197	**67**	½d vermilion ..	1·25	75	☐	☐
213		½d green*	1·25	1·00	☐	☐
198	**68**	1½d purple and green	13·00	5·00	☐	☐
200	**69**	2d green and red ..	20·00	9·00	☐	☐
201	**70**	2½d purple on blue	13·00	2·00	☐	☐
203	**71**	3d purple on yellow	18·00	2·50	☐	☐
205	**72**	4d green and brown	20·00	9·50	☐	☐
206	**73**	4½d green and red ..	7·00	28·00	☐	☐
207a	**74**	5d purple and blue	22·00	8·50	☐	☐
208	**75**	6d purple on red ..	20·00	8·50	☐	☐
209	**76**	9d purple and blue	48·00	30·00	☐	☐
210	**77**	10d purple and red	38·00	30·00	☐	☐
211	**78**	1s green	£180	50·00	☐	☐
214		1s green and red ..	45·00	£100	☐	☐
	Set of 14	.. .. ..	£375	£225	☐	☐

*The ½d. No. 213 in blue is a colour changeling

7

1902–13 *Wmks Imperial Crown Type* **49** (½*d to* 1*s*); *Anchor Type* **40** (2*s* 6*d to* 10*s*); *Three Crowns Type* **49** (£1)

(*a*) *Perf* 14

215	**79**	½d blue-green	75	50	□ □
217		½d yellow-green	75	50	□ □
219		1d red	75	50	□ □
221	**80**	1½d purple and green ..	14·00	7·50	□ □
291	**81**	2d green and red ..	13·00	7·50	□ □
231	**82**	2½d blue	6·00	3·50	□ □
232	**83**	3d purple on yellow ..	19·00	3·50	□ □
236a	**84**	4d green and brown ..	20·00	8·00	□ □
240		4d orange	9·00	8·50	□ □
294	**85**	5d purple and blue ..	14·00	7·50	□ □
246	**79**	6d purple	17·00	6·50	□ □
249	**86**	7d grey	5·00	7·00	□ □
307	**87**	9d purple and blue ..	32·00	27·00	□ □
311	**88**	10d purple and red ..	38·00	27·00	□ □
314	**89**	1s green and red ..	30·00	14·00	□ □
260	**90**	2s 6d lilac	£125	60·00	□ □
263	**91**	5s red	£140	70·00	□ □
265	**92**	10s blue	£375	£240	□ □
266	**93**	£1 green	£900	£375	□ □
		Set of 15 (*to* 1*s*)	£190	£110	□ □

(*b*) *Perf* 15 × 14

279	**79**	½d green	25·00	27·00	□ □
281		1d red	8·50	8·00	□ □
283	**82**	2½d blue	13·00	6·00	□ □
285	**83**	3d purple on yellow ..	20·00	5·00	□ □
286	**84**	4d orange	14·00	7·50	□ □
		Set of 5	70·00	48·00	□ □

KING GEORGE V
1910 (6 May)–1936 (20 Jan.)

PERFORATION. All the following issues are Perf 15 × 14 except vertical commemorative stamps which are 14 × 15, unless otherwise stated.

94 (Hair dark)   **95** (Lion unshaded)   **96**

1911–12 *Wmk Imperial Crown Type* **49**

322	**94**	½d green	3·00	1·50	□ □
327	**95**	1d red	3·00	1·50	□ □

1912 *Wmk Royal Cypher* ('Simple') *Type* **96**

335	**94**	½d green	28·00	30·00	□ □
336	**95**	1d red·	18·00	18·00	□ □

97 (Hair light)   **98** (Lion shaded)   **99**

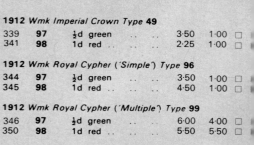

1912 *Wmk Imperial Crown Type* **49**

339	**97**	½d green	3·50	1·00	□
341	**98**	1d red	2·25	1·00	□

1912 *Wmk Royal Cypher* ('Simple') *Type* **96**

344	**97**	½d green	3·50	1·00	□
345	**98**	1d red	4·50	1·00	□

1912 *Wmk Royal Cypher* ('Multiple') *Type* **99**

346	**97**	½d green	6·00	4·00	□
350	**98**	1d red	5·50	5·50	□

100   **101**   **102**

103   **104**

1912–24 *Wmk Royal Cypher Type* **96**

351	**101**	½d green	50	35	□ □
357	**100**	1d red	50	25	□ □
362	**101**	1½d brown	1·75	40	□ □
368	**102**	2d orange	1·50	60	□ □
371	**100**	2½d blue	5·50	1·50	□ □
375	**102**	3d violet	2·25	1·25	□ □
379		4d grey-green ..	5·00	1·25	□ □
381	**103**	5d brown	4·50	3·50	□ □
385		6d purple	6·50	2·50	□ □
		a. Perf 14	65·00	£100	□ □
387		7d olive-green ..	10·00	5·00	□ □
390		8d black on yellow ..	20·00	8·50	□ □
392	**104**	9d black	12·00	3·25	□ □
393a		9d olive-green ..	70·00	20·00	□ □
394		10d blue	10·00	14·00	□ □
395		1s brown	10·00	1·25	□ □
		Set of 15	£140	55·00	□ □

1913 Wmk Royal Cypher ('Multiple') Type 99

397	**101**	½d green		£150	£180	☐ ☐
398	**100**	1d red		£225	£225	☐ ☐

See also Nos. 418/29.

105

106

T 105. Background around portrait consists of horizontal lines

1913–18 Wmk Single Cypher Type **106**   Perf 11 · 12

413*a*	**105**	2s 6d brown		65·00	35·00	☐ ☐
416		5s red		£175	50·00	☐ ☐
417		10s blue		£240	95·00	☐ ☐
403		£1 green		£1200	£700	☐ ☐
	Set of 4			£1500	£800	☐ ☐

See also Nos. 450/2.

107

1924–26 Wmk Block Cypher Type **107**

418	**101**	½d green		40	25	☐ ☐
419	**100**	1d red		40	25	☐ ☐
420	**101**	1½d brown		40	25	☐ ☐
421	**102**	2d orange		1·50	1·25	☐ ☐
422	**100**	2½d blue		3·25	1·50	☐ ☐
423	**102**	3d violet		5·50	1·50	☐ ☐
424		4d grey-green		7·00	1·25	☐ ☐
425	**103**	5d brown		11·00	2·00	☐ ☐
426*a*		6d purple		2·00	75	☐ ☐
427	**104**	9d olive-green		7·00	2·50	☐ ☐
428		10d blue		22·00	22·00	☐ ☐
429		1s brown		13·00	1·75	☐ ☐
	Set of 12			65·00	32·00	☐ ☐

For full information on all future British issues, collectors should write to the British Post Office Philatelic Bureau, 20 Brandon Street, Edinburgh EH3 5TT

108

109

British Empire Exhibition

1924–25 Wmk **107**   Perf 14

	(a) 23.4.24.	*Dated '1924'*				
430	**108**	1d red		6·00	9·00	☐ ☐
431	**109**	1½d brown		9·00	13·00	☐ ☐
	First Day Cover				£350	☐
	(b) 9.5.25.	*Dated '1925'*				
432	**108**	1d red		10·00	20·00	☐ ☐
433	**109**	1½d brown		30·00	55·00	☐ ☐
	First Day Cover				£1200	☐

110

111

112

113 St George and the Dragon

114

9

Ninth Universal Postal Union Congress

1929 (10 MAY) (a) *Wmk* **107**

434	**110**	½d green.		2·00	2·00	□ □
435	**111**	1d red		2·00	2·00	□ □
436		1½d brown		1·75	1·50	□ □
437	**112**	2½d blue		10·00	10·00	□ □

(b) *Wmk* **114** *Perf* 12

438	**113**	£1 black		£650	£450	□ □
434/7	*Set of 4*			14·00	14·00	□ □
434/7	*First Day Cover* (4 vals.)				£500	□
434/8	*First Day Cover* (5 vals.)				£3250	□

115

116

117

118

119

1934–36 *Wmk* **107**

439	**115**	½d green		10	25	□ □
440	**116**	1d red		15	25	□ □
441	**115**	1½d brown		10	25	□ □
442	**117**	2d orange		30	50	□ □
443	**116**	2½d blue		1·25	1·00	□ □
444	**117**	3d violet		1·25	1·00	□ □
445		4d grey-green		1·75	1·00	□ □
446	**118**	5d brown		6·00	2·50	□ □
447	**119**	9d olive-green		12·00	2·00	□ □
448		10d blue		15·00	10·00	□ □
449		1s brown		15·00	1·00	□ □
	Set of 11			48·00	18·00	□ □

T 105 *(re-engraved). Background around portrait consists of horizontal and diagonal lines*

1934 *Wmk* **106** *Perf* 11 × 12

450	**105**	2s 6d brown		55·00	25·00	□ □
451		5s red		£110	70·00	□ □
452		10s blue		£275	60·00	□ □
	Set of 3			£400	£140	□ □

120

121

122

123

Silver Jubilee

1935 (7 MAY) *Wmk* **107**

453	**120**	½d green		50	40	□ □
454	**121**	1d red		1·25	1·50	□ □
455	**122**	1½d brown		50	40	□ □
456	**123**	2½d blue		4·50	5·50	□ □
	Set of 4			6·00	7·00	□ □
	First Day Cover				£500	□

KING EDWARD VIII
1936 (20 Jan.–10 Dec.)

124

125

1936 *Wmk* **125**

457	**124**	½d green		20	20	□ □
458		1d red		50	25	□ □
459		1½d brown		25	20	□ □
460		2½d blue		25	75	□ □
	Set of 4			1·00	1·25	□ □

KING GEORGE VI
1936 (11 Dec.)–1952 (6 Feb.)

126 King George VI
and Queen Elizabeth

127

131 King George VI

131a

132

132a

Coronation

1937 (13 MAY) *Wmk* **127**

461	**126**	1½d brown		50	30	☐ ☐
		First Day Cover			28·00	☐

128

129

130

King George VI and National Emblems

133

1939–48 *Wmk* **133** *Perf* 14

476	**131**	2s 6d brown	38·00	6·50	☐ ☐
476a		2s 6d green	7·00	1·25	☐ ☐
477	**131a**	5s red	14·00	1·75	☐ ☐
478	**132**	10s dark blue	£170	21·00	☐ ☐
478a		10s bright blue	35·00	5·50	☐ ☐
478b	**132a**	£1 brown	10·00	23·00	☐ ☐
	Set of 6		£250	55·00	☐ ☐

1937–47 *Wmk* **127**

462	**128**	½d green		10	15	☐ ☐
463		1d scarlet		10	15	☐ ☐
464		1½d brown		20	15	☐ ☐
465		2d orange		75	50	☐ ☐
466		2½d blue		25	15	☐ ☐
467		3d violet		3·25	90	☐ ☐
468	**129**	4d green		50	50	☐ ☐
469		5d brown		2·00	60	☐ ☐
470		6d purple		1·25	50	☐ ☐
471	**130**	7d green		3·25	60	☐ ☐
472		8d red		3·50	60	☐ ☐
473		9d deep green		5·50	70	☐ ☐
474		10d blue		5·00	70	☐ ☐
474a		11d plum		2·00	1·75	☐ ☐
475		1s brown		5·75	60	☐ ☐
	Set of 15			30·00	7·50	☐ ☐

For later printings of the lower values in apparently lighter
shades and different colours, see Nos. 485/90 and 503/8.

134 Queen Victoria and King George VI

Centenary of First Adhesive Postage Stamps

1940 (6 MAY) *Wmk* **127** *Perf* 14½ × 14

479	**134**	½d green	30	30	☐ ☐
480		1d red	1·00	50	☐ ☐
481		1½d brown	30	40	☐ ☐
482		2d orange	50	50	☐ ☐
483		2½d blue	2·25	90	☐ ☐
484		3d violet	3·00	3·25	☐ ☐
	Set of 6		6·50	5·25	☐ ☐
	First Day Cover			45·00	☐

For full information on all future British issues, collectors
should write to the British Post Office Philatelic Bureau, 20
Brandon Street, Edinburgh EH3 5TT

Head as Nos. 462 7, but lighter background

1941–42 *Wmk* **127**

485	128	½d pale green	20	20	☐	☐
486		1d pale red	20	20	☐	☐
487		1½d pale brown	85	55	☐	☐
488		2d pale orange	60	50	☐	☐
489		2½d light blue	25	20	☐	☐
490		3d pale violet	1·75	60	☐	☐
		Set of 6	3·50	2·00	☐	☐

135 Symbols of Peace and Reconstruction

136 Symbols of Peace and Reconstruction

Victory

1946 (11 JUNE) *Wmk* **127**

491	135	2½d blue	30	20	☐	☐
492	136	3d violet	30	20	☐	☐
		First Day Cover		60·00		☐

137 King George VI and Queen Elizabeth

138 King George VI and Queen Elizabeth

Royal Silver Wedding

1948 (26 APR.) *Wmk* **127**

493	137	2½d blue	30	30	☐	☐
494	138	£1 blue	38·00	35·00	☐	☐
		First Day Cover		£350		☐

1948 (10 MAY)

Stamps of 1d and 2½d showing seaweed-gathering were on sale at eight Head Post Offices elsewhere in Great Britain, but were primarily for use in the Channel Islands and are listed there (see after Regional Issues).

139 Globe and Laurel Wreath

140 Speed

141 Olympic Symbol

142 Winged Victory

Olympic Games

1948 (29 JULY) *Wmk* **127**

495	139	2½d blue	10	10	☐	☐
496	140	3d violet	30	30	☐	☐
497	141	6d purple	60	30	☐	☐
498	142	1s brown	1·25	1·50	☐	☐
		Set of 4	2·00	2·00	☐	☐
		First Day Cover		38·00		☐

143 Two Hemispheres

144 U P U Monument, Berne

145 Goddess Concordia, Globe and Points of Compass

146 Posthorn and Globe

75th Anniversary of Universal Postal Union

1949 (10 OCT.) *Wmk* **127**

499	143	2½d blue	10	10	☐	☐
500	144	3d violet	30	40	☐	☐
501	145	6d purple	60	75	☐	☐
502	146	1s brown	1·25	1·50	☐	☐
		Set of 4	2·00	2·75	☐	☐
		First Day Cover		55·00		☐

4d as No. 468 and others as Nos. 485/9, but colours changed

1950–51 *Wmk* **127**

503	**128**	½d pale orange	..	30	30	☐	☐
504		1d light blue		30	30	☐	☐
505		1½d pale green		35	50	☐	☐
506		2d pale brown		35	30	☐	☐
507		2½d pale red		35	30	☐	☐
508	**129**	4d light blue		2·25	1·50	☐	☐
	Set of 6	.. .. ..		3·50	2·75		

147 HMS *Victory*

148 White Cliffs of Dover

149 St George and the Dragon

150 Royal Coat of Arms

1951 (3 MAY) *Wmk* **133** *Perf* 11 × 12

509	**147**	2s 6d green	..	6·00	75	☐	☐
510	**148**	5s red ..		30·00	1·50	☐	☐
511	**149**	10s blue		20·00	8·00	☐	☐
512	**150**	£1 brown		30·00	18·00	☐	☐
	Set of 4			75·00	24·00	☐	☐

151 Commerce and Prosperity

152 Festival Symbol

Festival of Britain

1951 (3 MAY) *Wmk* **127**

513	**151**	2½d red	..	25	20	☐	☐
514	**152**	4d blue		50	45	☐	☐
	First Day Cover	.. ..		30·00		☐	

QUEEN ELIZABETH II
6 February, 1952

153 Tudor Crown

154

155

156

157

158

159

160

1952–54 *Wmk* **153**

515	**154**	½d orange	..	10	15	☐	☐
516		1d blue	..	20	20	☐	☐
517		1½d green	..	10	15	☐	☐
518		2d brown	..	20	15	☐	☐
519	**155**	2½d red ..		10	15	☐	☐
520		3d lilac	..	1·00	75	☐	☐
521	**156**	4d blue	..	3·00	1·25	☐	☐
		4½d (*See Nos.* 577, 594, 609 *and* 616*b*)					
522	**157**	5d brown	..	90	2·75	☐	☐
523		6d purple	..	3·00	90	☐	☐
524		7d green	..	9·00	5·00	☐	☐
525	**158**	8d magenta	..	1·00	1·00	☐	☐
526		9d bronze-green		22·00	3·75	☐	☐
527		10d blue	..	18·00	3·75	☐	☐
528		11d plum	..	30·00	20·00	☐	☐
529	**159**	1s bistre	..	1·25	60	☐	☐
530	**160**	1s 3d green	..	4·50	3·00	☐	☐
531	**159**	1s 6d indigo	..	11·00	3·50	☐	☐
	Set of 17			95·00	42·00	☐	☐

First Day Covers

5 Dec. 1952	Nos. 517, 519	.. ..	8·00 ☐
6 July 1953	Nos. 522, 525, 529	.. ..	40·00 ☐
31 Aug. 1953	Nos. 515/16, 518	.. ..	40·00 ☐
2 Nov. 1953	Nos. 521, 530/1	.. .. ..	£140 ☐
18 Jan. 1954	Nos. 520, 523/4	..	85·00 ☐
8 Feb. 1954	Nos. 526/8	.. ..	£170 ☐

See also Nos. 540/56, 561/6, 570/94 and 599/618*a*.

13

161

162

163

164

Coronation

1953 (3 JUNE) *Wmk* **153**

532	**161**	2½d red			10	50	☐ ☐
533	**162**	4d blue			40	1·75	☐ ☐
534	**163**	1s 3d green			3·50	2·75	☐ ☐
535	**164**	1s 6d blue			7·00	3·50	☐ ☐
		Set of 4			10·00	7·50	☐ ☐
		First Day Cover				48·00	☐

165 St Edward's Crown

166 Carrickfergus Castle

167 Caernarvon Castle

168 Edinburgh Castle

169 Windsor Castle

1955 (1–23 SEPT.) *Wmk* **165** *Perf* 11 × 12

536	**166**	2s 6d brown			10·00	2·00	☐ ☐
537	**167**	5s red			30·00	3·50	☐ ☐
538	**168**	10s blue			80·00	12·00	☐ ☐

539	**169**	£1 black			£130	38·00	☐ ☐
		Set of 4			£225	50·00	☐ ☐
		First Day Cover (Nos. 538/9)					
		(1 Sept.)				£500	☐
		First Day Cover (Nos. 536/7)					
		(23 Sept.)				£325	☐

See also Nos 595*a*/8*a* and 759/62.

1955–58 *Wmk* **165**

540	**154**	½d orange		10	15	☐ ☐
541		1d blue		25	15	☐ ☐
542		1½d green		25	25	☐ ☐
543		2d red-brown		20	25	☐ ☐
543*b*		2d light red-brown		20	25	☐ ☐
544	**155**	2½d red		20	25	☐ ☐
545		3d lilac		20	25	☐ ☐
546	**156**	4d blue		1·40	50	☐ ☐
547	**157**	5d brown		5·50	4·75	☐ ☐
548		6d purple		4·00	1·00	☐ ☐
549		7d green		50·00	9·00	☐ ☐
550	**158**	8d magenta		6·00	1·00	☐ ☐
551		9d bronze-green		23·00	2·75	☐ ☐
552		10d blue		19·00	2·75	☐ ☐
553		11d plum		50	1·50	☐ ☐
554	**159**	1s bistre		19·00	50	☐ ☐
555	**160**	1s 3d green		27·00	1·50	☐ ☐
556	**159**	1s 6d indigo		19·00	1·50	☐ ☐
		Set of 18		£150	23·00	☐ ☐

170 Scout Badge and Rolling Hitch

171 Scouts coming to Britain

172 Globe within a Compass

173

World Scout Jubilee Jamboree

1957 (1 AUG.) *Wmk* **165**

557	**170**	2½d red		15	25	☐ ☐
558	**171**	4d blue		50	1·25	☐ ☐
559	**172**	1s 3d green		5·00	4·75	☐ ☐
		Set of 3		5·00	5·50	☐ ☐
		First Day Cover			20·00	☐

46th Inter Parliamentary Union Conference

1957 (12 SEPT.) *Wmk* **165**

560	**173**	4d blue		1·00	1·25	☐ ☐
		First Day Cover			90·00	☐

Graphite-lined and Phosphor Issues

These are used in connection with automatic sorting machinery, originally experimentally at Southampton but now also operating elsewhere. In such areas these stamps were the normal issue, but from mid 1967 *all* low-value stamps bear phosphor markings.

The graphite lines were printed in black on the back, beneath the gum; two lines per stamp except for the 2d (*see below*).

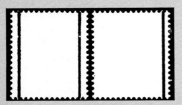

174   **175** (2d only)

(Stamps viewed from back)

In November 1959, phosphor bands, printed on the front, replaced the graphite. They are wider than the graphite, not easy to see, but show as broad vertical bands at certain angles to the light.

Values representing the rate for printed papers (and second class mail from 1968) have one band and others have two, three or four bands according to size and format. From 1972 onwards some commemorative stamps were printed with 'all-over' phosphor.

In the small stamps the bands are on each side with the single band at left (except where otherwise stated). In the large-size commemorative stamps the single band may be at left, centre or right varying in different issues. The bands are vertical on both horizontal and vertical designs except where otherwise stated.

See also notes on page 36.

Graphite-lined issue

1957 (19 Nov.) *Two graphite lines on the back, except 2d value, which has one line. Wmk* **165**

561	**154**	½d orange	.. ..	20	30	☐	☐
562		1d blue	.. ..	20	50	☐	☐
563		1½d green	.. ..	30	2·00	☐	☐
564		2d light red-brown	2·50	2·25	☐	☐
565	**155**	2½d red	.. ..	8·00	7·00	☐	☐
566		3d lilac	.. ..	30	70	☐	☐
	Set of 6	.. ..	10·50	11·50	☐	☐
	First Day Cover	.. ..		80·00		☐

See also Nos. 587/94.

176 Welsh Dragon

177 Flag and Games Emblem

178 Welsh Dragon

Sixth British Empire and Commonwealth Games, Cardiff

1958 (18 July) *Wmk* **165**

567	**176**	3d lilac	.. ..	15	10	☐	☐
568	**177**	6d mauve	.. ..	25	45	☐	☐
569	**178**	1s 3d green	.. ..	2·75	2·75	☐	☐
	Set of 3	.. .. ..	2·75	2·75	☐	☐
	First Day Cover	.. .. ..		60·00		☐

179 Multiple Crowns

WATERMARK. All the following issues to No. 755 are Watermark **179** (sideways on the vertical commemorative stamps) unless otherwise stated.

1958–65 *Wmk* **179**

570	**154**	½d orange	.. ..	10	10	☐	☐
571		1d blue	.. ..	10	10	☐	☐
572		1½d green	.. ..	10	15	☐	☐
573		2d light red-brown	10	10	☐	☐
574	**155**	2½d red	.. ..	10	10	☐	☐
575		3d lilac	.. ..	10	20	☐	☐
576a	**156**	4d blue	.. ..	15	10	☐	☐
577		4½d brown	.. ..	10	30	☐	☐
578	**157**	5d brown	.. ..	25	40	☐	☐
579		6d purple	.. ..	40	30	☐	☐
580		7d green	.. ..	40	60	☐	☐
581	**158**	8d magenta	.. ..	40	30	☐	☐
582		9d bronze-green	..	40	50	☐	☐
583		10d blue	.. ..	1·00	50	☐	☐
584	**159**	1s bistre	.. ..	50	30	☐	☐
585	**160**	1s 3d green	.. ..	25	30	☐	☐
586	**159**	1s 6d indigo	.. ..	4·00	40	☐	☐
	Set of 17	.. ..	8·00	4·25	☐	☐
	First Day Cover (*No.* 577) (9 Feb. 1959)		£150		☐

For full information on all future British issues, collectors should write to the British Post Office Philatelic Bureau, 20 Brandon Street, Edinburgh EH3 5TT

15

Graphite-lined issue

1958–59 Two graphite lines on the back, except 2d value, which has one line. Wmk **179**

587	**154**	½d orange			1·25	2·25	☐	☐
588		1d blue			1·00	1·50	☐	☐
589		1½d green			40·00	40·00	☐	☐
590		2d light red-brown			6·00	3·25	☐	☐
591	**155**	2½d red			8·00	10·00	☐	☐
592		3d lilac			50	50	☐	☐
593	**156**	4d blue			3·50	4·50	☐	☐
594		4½d brown			5·00	4·00	☐	☐
	Set of 8				60·00	60·00	☐	☐

The prices quoted for Nos. 587 and 589 are for examples with inverted watermark. Stamps with upright watermark are priced at: ½d. £7 mint or used and 1½d £95 *mint*, £60 *used*.

1959–63 Wmk **179**   Perf 11 × 12

595a	**166**	2s 6d brown		50	30	☐	☐
596a	**167**	5s red		1·00	60	☐	☐
597a	**168**	10s blue		3·00	3·50	☐	☐
598a	**169**	£1 black		8·00	5·50	☐	☐
	Set of 4			11·00	9·00	☐	☐

Phosphor-Graphite issue

1959 (18 Nov.) Two phosphor bands on front and two graphite lines on back, except 2d value, which has one band on front and one line on back

(a) Wmk **165**

599	**154**	½d orange		4·00	6·00	☐	☐
600		1d blue		8·00	7·00	☐	☐
601		1½d green		2·00	6·00	☐	☐

(b) Wmk **179**

605	**154**	2d light red-brown (1 band)		4·50	4·00	☐	☐
606	**155**	2½d red		20·00	13·00	☐	☐
607		3d lilac		9·00	8·00	☐	☐
608	**156**	4d blue		12·00	25·00	☐	☐
609		4½d brown		35·00	15·00	☐	☐
	Set of 8			80·00	70·00	☐	☐

Phosphor issue

1960–67 Two phosphor bands on front, except where otherwise stated. Wmk **179**

610	**154**	½d orange		10	15	☐	☐
611		1d blue		10	10	☐	☐
612		1½d green		10	20	☐	☐
613		2d light red-brown (1 band)		22·00	19·00	☐	☐
613a		2d light red-brown (2 bands)		10	10	☐	☐
614	**155**	2½d red (2 bands)		10	10	☐	☐
614a		2½d red (1 band)		50	1·00	☐	☐
615		3d lilac (2 bands)		60	75	☐	☐
615c		3d lilac (1 side band)		50	75	☐	☐
615e		3d lilac (1 centre band)		25	40	☐	☐

616a	**156**	4d blue		30	30	☐	☐
616b		4½d brown		30	30	☐	☐
616c	**157**	5d brown		30	30	☐	☐
617		6d purple		30	50	☐	☐
617a		7d green		60	30	☐	☐
617b	**158**	8d magenta		20	30	☐	☐
617c		9d bronze-green		60	30	☐	☐
617d		10d blue		80	35	☐	☐
617e	**159**	1s bistre		40	40	☐	☐
618	**160**	1s 3d green		1·75	2·75	☐	☐
618a	**159**	1s 6d indigo		2·00	1·25	☐	☐
	Set of 17 (one of each value)			7·00	6·50	☐	☐

No. 615c exists with the phosphor band at the left or right of the stamp.

180 Postboy of 1660   **181** Posthorn of 1660

Tercentenary of Establishment of 'General Letter Office'

1960 (7 July)

619	**180**	3d lilac		20	10	☐	☐
620	**181**	1s 3d green		3·75	3·75	☐	☐
	Set of 2			3·75	3·75	☐	☐
	First Day Cover				48·00		☐

182 Conference Emblem

First Anniversary of European Postal and Telecommunications Conference

1960 (19 Sept.)

621	**182**	6d green and purple		40	60	☐	☐
622		1s 6d brown and blue		6·50	5·00	☐	☐
	Set of 2			6·75	5·50	☐	☐
	First Day Cover				40·00		☐

183 Thrift Plant   **184** Growth of Savings

185 Thrift Plant

Centenary of Post Office Savings Bank

1961 (28 Aug.)

623	**183**	2½d black and red	20	20	☐	☐
624	**184**	3d orange-brown and violet	20	20	☐	☐
625	**185**	1s 6d red and blue	2·75	2·25	☐	☐
		Set of 3	2·75	2·25	☐	☐
		First Day Cover		60·00		☐

186 C E P T Emblem

187 Doves and Emblem

188 Doves and Emblem

European Postal and Telecommunications (C.E.P.T.) Conference, Torquay

1961 (18 Sept.)

626	**186**	2d orange, pink and brown	20	15	☐	☐
627	**187**	4d buff, mauve and ultramarine	20	15	☐	☐
628	**188**	10d turquoise, green and blue	50	55	☐	☐
		Set of 3	75	75	☐	☐
		First Day Cover		6·00		☐

189 Hammer Beam Roof, Westminster Hall

190 Palace of Westminster

Seventh Commonwealth Parliamentary Conference

1961 (25 Sept.)

629	**189**	6d purple and gold	25	25	☐	☐
630	**190**	1s 3d green and blue	2·75	2·50	☐	☐
		Set of 2	3·00	2·75	☐	☐
		First Day Cover		26·00		☐

191 'Units of Productivity'

192 'National Productivity'

193 Unified Productivity'

National Productivity Year

1962 (14 Nov.) *Wmk* **179** (*inverted on 2½d and 3d*)

631	**191**	2½d green and red	20	10	☐	☐
		p. Phosphor	1·00	50	☐	☐
632	**192**	3d blue and violet	25	10	☐	☐
		p. Phosphor	1·00	50	☐	☐
633	**193**	1s 3d red, blue and green	1·75	2·00	☐	☐
		p. Phosphor	22·00	30·00	☐	☐
		Set of 3 (Ordinary)	2·00	2·00	☐	☐
		Set of 3 (Phosphor)	22·00	30·00	☐	☐
		First Day Cover (Ordinary)		45·00		☐
		First Day Cover (Phosphor)		85·00		☐

194 Campaign Emblem and Family

195 Children of Three Races

Freedom from Hunger

1963 (21 Mar.) *Wmk* **179** (*inverted*)

634	**194**	2½d crimson and pink	10	10	☐	☐
		p. Phosphor	1·00	1·25	☐	☐
635	**195**	1s 3d brown and yellow	2·00	2·00	☐	☐
		p. Phosphor	22·00	30·00	☐	☐
		Set of 2 (Ordinary)	2·00	2·00	☐	☐
		Set of 2 (Phosphor)	22·00	30·00	☐	☐
		First Day Cover (Ordinary)		32·00		☐
		First Day Cover (Phosphor)		38·00		☐

196 Paris Conference

Paris Postal Conference Centenary

1963 (7 May) *Wmk 179 (inverted)*

636	**196**	6d green and mauve	50	50	☐	☐
		p Phosphor	6·50	6·50	☐	☐
		First Day Cover (Ordinary)		14·00	☐
		First Day Cover (Phosphor)		28·00	☐

197 Posy of Flowers

198 Woodland Life

National Nature Week

1963 (16 May)

637	**197**	3d multicoloured	25	20	☐	☐
		p Phosphor	50	60	☐	☐
638	**198**	4½d multicoloured	40	50	☐	☐
		p Phosphor	2·50	2·50	☐	☐
		Set of 2 (Ordinary)	60	70	☐	☐
		Set of 2 (Phosphor)	3·00	3·00	☐	☐
		First Day Cover (Ordinary)		22·00	☐
		First Day Cover (Phosphor)		27·00	☐

199 Rescue at Sea

200 19th-century Lifeboat

201 Lifeboatmen

202 Red Cross

203

204

205 Commonwealth Cable

Ninth International Lifeboat Conference, Edinburgh

1963 (31 May)

639	**199**	2½d blue, black and red	10	10	☐	☐
		p Phosphor	40	50	☐	☐
640	**200**	4d multicoloured	40	30	☐	☐
		p Phosphor	20	50	☐	☐
641	**201**	1s 6d sepia, yellow and blue	2·50	2·75	☐	☐
		p Phosphor	48·00	30·00	☐	☐
		Set of 3 (Ordinary)	2·75	2·75	☐	☐
		Set of 3 (Phosphor)	48·00	30·00	☐	☐
		First Day Cover (Ordinary)		30·00	☐
		First Day Cover (Phosphor)		38·00	☐

Red Cross Centenary Congress

1963 (15 Aug.)

642	**202**	3d red and lilac	10	10	☐	☐
		p Phosphor	60	60	☐	☐
643	**203**	1s 3d red, blue and grey	3·25	2·75	☐	☐
		p Phosphor	40·00	38·00	☐	☐
644	**204**	1s 6d red, blue and bistre	3·00	2·75	☐	☐
		p Phosphor	35·00	30·00	☐	☐
		Set of 3 (Ordinary)	6·00	5·00	☐	☐
		Set of 3 (Phosphor)	70·00	60·00	☐	☐
		First Day Cover (Ordinary)		35·00	☐
		First Day Cover (Phosphor)		65·00	☐

Opening of COMPAC (Trans-Pacific Telephone Cable)

1963 (3 Dec.)

645	**205**	1s 6d blue and black	2·25	2·25	☐	☐
		p Phosphor	18·00	18·00	☐	☐
		First Day Cover (Ordinary)		22·00	☐
		First Day Cover (Phosphor)		28·00	☐

206 Puck and Bottom
(*A Midsummer Night's Dream*)

207 Feste (*Twelfth Night*)

208 Balcony Scene
(*Romeo and Juliet*)

209 Eve of Agincourt
(*Henry V*)

210 Hamlet contemplating
Yorick's skull (*Hamlet*)
and Queen Elizabeth II

Shakespeare Festival

1964 (23 APR) Perf 11 · 12 (2s 6d) or 15 · 14 (others)

646	**206**	3d bis, blk & vio-bl	10	10	☐	☐
		p Phosphor	20	30	☐	☐
647	**207**	6d multicoloured	20	30	☐	☐
		p Phosphor	60	90	☐	☐
648	**208**	1s 3d multicoloured	90	1·00	☐	☐
		p Phosphor	5·75	6·50	☐	☐
649	**209**	1s 6d multicoloured	1·25	1·00	☐	☐
		p Phosphor	11·00	6·75	☐	☐
650	**210**	2s 6d deep slate-purple	2·00	2·25	☐	☐
		Set of 5 (Ordinary)	4·00	4·25	☐	☐
		Set of 4 (Phosphor)	15·00	13·00	☐	☐
		First Day Cover (Ordinary)		8·50		☐
		First Day Cover (Phosphor)		15·00		☐
		Presentation Pack (Ordinary)	10·00		☐	

PRESENTATION PACKS were first introduced by the G P O. for the Shakespeare Festival issue. The packs include one set of stamps and details of the designs, the designer and the stamp printer. They were issued for almost all later definitive and special issues

211 Flats near Richmond Park
('Urban Development')

212 Shipbuilding Yards, Belfast
('Industrial Activity')

213 Beddgelert Forest Park,
Snowdonia (Forestry)

214 Nuclear Reactor, Dounreay
(Technological Development)

20th International Geographical Congress, London

1964 (1 JULY)

651	**211**	2½d multicoloured	10	10	☐	☐
		p Phosphor	50	40	☐	☐
652	**212**	4d multicoloured	25	25	☐	☐
		p Phosphor	75	70	☐	☐
653	**213**	8d multicoloured	60	50	☐	☐
		p Phosphor	1·75	1·50	☐	☐
654	**214**	1s 6d multicoloured	3·25	3·25	☐	☐
		p Phosphor	26·00	21·00	☐	☐
		Set of 4 (Ordinary)	4·00	4·00	☐	☐
		Set of 4 (Phosphor)	26·00	21·00	☐	☐
		First Day Cover (Ordinary)		19·00		☐
		First Day Cover (Phosphor)		29·00		☐
		Presentation Pack (Ordinary)	£100		☐	

215 Spring Gentian

216 Dog Rose

217 Honeysuckle

218 Fringed Water Lily

Tenth International Botanical Congress, Edinburgh

1964 (5 AUG.)

655	**215**	3d vio. blue & green	10	10	☐	☐
		p Phosphor	20	30	☐	☐
656	**216**	6d multicoloured	20	20	☐	☐
		p Phosphor	2·00	1·50	☐	☐
657	**217**	9d multicoloured	1·60	2·50	☐	☐
		p Phosphor	4·50	3·00	☐	☐
658	**218**	1s 3d multicoloured	2·50	1·90	☐	☐
		p Phosphor	24·00	20·00	☐	☐
		Set of 4 (Ordinary)	4·00	4·00	☐	☐
		Set of 4 (Phosphor)	28·00	22·00	☐	☐
		First Day Cover (Ordinary)		25·00		☐
		First Day Cover (Phosphor)		35·00		☐
		Presentation Pack (Ordinary)	£100		☐	

219 Forth Road Bridge

220 Forth Road and Railway Bridges

Opening of Forth Road Bridge

1964 (4 SEPT.)

659	**219**	3d	black, blue and violet	15	10	☐	☐
		p	*Phosphor*	50	50	☐	☐
660	**220**	6d	black, blue and red	45	40	☐	☐
		p	*Phosphor*	4·75	4·75	☐	☐
			Set of 2 (Ordinary)	60	50	☐	☐
			Set of 2 (Phosphor)	5·25	5·25	☐	☐
			First Day Cover (Ordinary)		7·50		☐
			First Day Cover (Phosphor)		11·00		☐
			Presentation Pack (Ordinary)	£250		☐	

221 Sir Winston Churchill

222 Sir Winston Churchill

Churchill Commemoration

1965 (8 JULY)

661	**221**	4d	black and drab	15	10	☐	☐
		p	*Phosphor*	30	30	☐	☐
662	**222**	1s 3d	black and grey	45	40	☐	☐
		p	*Phosphor*	3·50	3·50	☐	☐
			Set of 2 (Ordinary)	60	50	☐	☐
			Set of 2 (Phosphor)	3·75	3·75	☐	☐
			First Day Cover (Ordinary)		5·00		☐
			First Day Cover (Phosphor)		7·50		☐
			Presentation Pack (Ordinary)	16·00		☐	

223 Simon de Montfort's Seal

224 Parliament Buildings
(after engraving by Hollar 1647)

700th Anniversary of Simon de Montfort's Parliament

1965 (19 JULY)

663	**223**	6d	green	10	10	☐	☐
		p	*Phosphor*	1·00	1·00	☐	☐
664	**224**	2s 6d	black, grey and drab	1·25	1·25	☐	☐
			Set of 2 (Ordinary)	1·25	1·25	☐	☐
			First Day Cover (Ordinary)		11·00		☐
			First Day Cover (Phosphor)		16·00		☐
			Presentation Pack (Ordinary)	35·00		☐	

225 Bandsmen and Banner

226 Three Salvationists

Salvation Army Centenary

1965 (9 AUG.)

665	**225**	3d	multicoloured	10	10	☐	☐
		p	*Phosphor*	50	40	☐	☐
666	**226**	1s 6d	multicoloured	1·00	1·00	☐	☐
		p	*Phosphor*	3·00	3·25	☐	☐
			Set of 2 (Ordinary)	1·10	1·10	☐	☐
			Set of 2 (Phosphor)	3·50	3·50	☐	☐
			First Day Cover (Ordinary)		21·00		☐
			First Day Cover (Phosphor)		28·00		☐

227 Lister's Carbolic Spray

228 Lister and Chemical Symbols

Centenary of Joseph Lister's Discovery of Antiseptic Surgery

1965 (1 SEPT.)

667	**227**	4d	indigo, chestnut and grey	10	10	☐	☐
		p	*Phosphor*	15	20	☐	☐
668	**228**	1s	black, purple and blue	1·00	1·50	☐	☐
		p	*Phosphor*	2·75	2·75	☐	☐
			Set of 2 (Ordinary)	1·10	1·50	☐	☐
			Set of 2 (Phosphor)	2·75	2·75	☐	☐
			First Day Cover (Ordinary)		12·00		☐
			First Day Cover (Phosphor)		13·00		☐

229 Trinidad Carnival Dancers   **230** Canadian Folk dancers

Commonwealth Arts Festival

1965 (1 Sept.)

669	**229**	6d	black and orange	10	10	☐	☐
		p	Phosphor	30	30	☐	☐
670	**230**	1s 6d	black and violet	1·25	1·50	☐	☐
		p	Phosphor	2·50	2·50	☐	☐
			Set of 2 (Ordinary)	1·25	1·50	☐	☐
			Set of 2 (Phosphor)	2·75	2·75	☐	☐
			First Day Cover (Ordinary)		15·00		☐
			First Day Cover (Phosphor)		21·00		☐

231 Flight of Supermarine Spitfires

232 Pilot in Hawker Hurricane Mk I

233 Wing-tips of Supermarine Spitfire and Messerschmitt Bf 109

234 Supermarine Spitfires attacking Heinkel HE 111H Bomber

235 Supermarine Spitfire attacking Junkers Ju 87B "Stuka" Dive-bomber

236 Hawker Hurricanes Mk I over Wreck of Dornier Do-17Z Bomber

The above were issued together se-tenant in blocks of six (3 × 2) within the sheet.

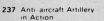   

237 Anti-aircraft Artillery in Action

238 Air battle over St Paul's Cathedral

25th Anniversary of Battle of Britain

1965 (13 Sept.)

671	**231**	4d	olive and black	30	35	☐	☐
	a		Block of 6				
			Nos 671/6	7·00	9·00	☐	☐
		p	Phosphor	40	50	☐	☐
	pa		Block of 6				
			Nos 671p/6p	12·00	14·00	☐	☐
672	**232**	4d	olive, blackish olive and black	30	35	☐	☐
		p	Phosphor	40	50	☐	☐
673	**233**	4d	multicoloured	30	35	☐	☐
		p	Phosphor	40	50	☐	☐
674	**234**	4d	olive and black	30	35	☐	☐
		p	Phosphor	40	50	☐	☐
675	**235**	4d	olive and black	30	35	☐	☐
		p	Phosphor	40	50	☐	☐
676	**236**	4d	multicoloured	30	35	☐	☐
		p	Phosphor	40	50	☐	☐
677	**237**	9d	violet, orange and purple	1·25	1·25	☐	☐
		p	Phosphor	1·25	80	☐	☐
678	**238**	1s 3d	multicoloured	1·25	1·25	☐	☐
		p	Phosphor	1·25	80	☐	☐
			Set of 8 (Ordinary)	8·50	4·25		☐
			Set of 8 (Phosphor)	14·00	4·25		☐
			First Day Cover (Ordinary)		24·00		☐
			First Day Cover (Phosphor)		24·00		☐
			Presentation Pack (Ordinary)	48·00			☐

239 Tower and Georgian Buildings   **240** Tower and Nash Terrace. Regent's Park

Opening of Post Office Tower

1965 (8 Oct.)

679	**239**	3d	yellow, blue and green	10	10	☐	☐
		p	Phosphor	10	10	☐	☐
680	**240**	1s 3d	green and blue	65	75	☐	☐
		p	Phosphor	50	50	☐	☐
			Set of 2 (Ordinary)	75	85	☐	☐
			Set of 2 (Phosphor)	60	60	☐	☐
			First Day Cover (Ordinary)		7·00		☐
			First Day Cover (Phosphor)		9·00		☐
			Presentation Pack (Ordinary)	3·50		☐	
			Presentation Pack (Phosphor)	3·50		☐	

241 U N Emblem   **242** I C Y Emblem

20th Anniversary of UNO and International Co-operation Year

1965 (25 Oct)

681	**241**	3d	blk, orge & bl	15	20	☐	☐
		p	*Phosphor*	25	40	☐	☐
682	**242**	1s 6d	blk, pur & bl	1·10	1·10	☐	☐
		p	*Phosphor*	3·50	3·50	☐	☐
		Set of 2 (Ordinary)		1·25	1·25	☐	☐
		Set of 2 (Phosphor)		3·75	3·75	☐	☐
		First Day Cover (Ordinary)			12·00		☐
		First Day Cover (Phosphor)			14·00		☐

243 Telecommunications Network   **244** Radio Waves and Switchboard

I.T.U. Centenary

1965 (15 Nov.)

683	**243**	9d	multicoloured	20	25	☐	☐
		p	*Phosphor*	60	50	☐	☐
684	**244**	1s 6d	multicoloured	1·60	1·50	☐	☐
		p	*Phosphor*	5·25	5·25	☐	☐
		Set of 2 (Ordinary)		1·75	1·75	☐	☐
		Set of 2 (Phosphor)		5·75	5·75	☐	☐
		First Day Cover (Ordinary)			16·00		☐
		First Day Cover (Phosphor)			18·00		☐

245 Robert Burns (after Skirving chalk drawing)   **246** Robert Burns (after Nasmyth portrait)

Burns Commemoration

1966 (25 Jan.)

685	**245**	4d	blk, indigo & bl	15	15	☐	☐
		p	*Phosphor*	25	25	☐	☐
686	**246**	1s 3d	blk, bl & orge	70	70	☐	☐
		p	*Phosphor*	2·25	2·25	☐	☐
		Set of 2 (Ordinary)		85	85	☐	☐
		Set of 2 (Phosphor)		2·50	2·50	☐	☐
		First Day Cover (Ordinary)			4·00		☐
		First Day Cover (Phosphor)			5·00		☐
		Presentation Pack (Ordinary)		40·00		☐	

247 Westminster Abbey   **248** Fan Vaulting. Henry VII Chapel

900th Anniversary of Westminster Abbey

1966 (28 Feb.)   *Perf 15 × 14 (3d) or 11 × 12 (2s 6d)*

687	**247**	3d	black, brown and blue	15	20	☐	☐
		p	*Phosphor*	30	30	☐	☐
688	**248**	2s 6d	black	85	1·10	☐	☐
		Set of 2		1·00	1·25	☐	☐
		First Day Cover (Ordinary)			7·50		☐
		First Day Cover (Phosphor)			11·00		☐
		Presentation Pack (Ordinary)		16·00		☐	

249 View near Hassocks. Sussex   **250** Antrim. Northern Ireland

251 Harlech Castle, Wales   **252** Cairngorm Mountains. Scotland

Landscapes

1966 (2 May)

689	**249**	4d	black, yellow-green and blue	15	15	☐	☐
		p	*Phosphor*	15	15	☐	☐
690	**250**	6d	black, green and blue	15	15	☐	☐
		p	*Phosphor*	25	25	☐	☐
691	**251**	1s 3d	black, yellow and blue	35	35	☐	☐
		p	*Phosphor*	35	35	☐	☐
692	**252**	1s 6d	black, orange and blue	50	50	☐	☐
		p	*Phosphor*	50	50	☐	☐
		Set of 4 (Ordinary)		1·00	1·00	☐	☐
		Set of 4 (Phosphor)		1·00	1·00	☐	☐
		First Day Cover (Ordinary)			9·50		☐
		First Day Cover (Phosphor)			9·50		☐

253 Players with Ball

260 Cup Winners

254 Goalmouth Mêlée

255 Goalkeeper saving Goal

World Cup Football Championship

1966 (1 JUNE)

693	**253**	4d multicoloured	15	10	☐	☐
	p	Phosphor	15	10	☐	☐
694	**254**	6d multicoloured	20	20	☐	☐
	p	Phosphor	20	20	☐	☐
695	**255**	1s 3d multicoloured	75	75	☐	☐
	p	Phosphor	75	75	☐	☐
		Set of 3 (Ordinary)	1·00	1·00	☐	☐
		Set of 3 (Phosphor)	1·00	1·00	☐	☐
		First Day Cover (Ordinary)		11·00	☐	
		First Day Cover (Phosphor)		15·00	☐	
		Presentation Pack (Ordinary)	14·00		☐	

256 Black-headed Gull

257 Blue Tit

258 Robin

259 Blackbird

The above were issued *se-tenant* in blocks of four within the sheet.

British Birds

1966 (8 AUG.)

696	**256**	4d multicoloured	10	15	☐	☐
	a	Block of 4				
		Nos 696/9	1·00	1·25	☐	☐
	p	Phosphor	10	15	☐	☐
	pa	Block of 4				
		Nos 696p/9p	1·00	1·00	☐	☐
697	**257**	4d multicoloured	10	15	☐	☐
	p	Phosphor	10	15	☐	☐
698	**258**	4d multicoloured	10	15	☐	☐
	p	Phosphor	10	15	☐	☐
699	**259**	4d multicoloured	10	15	☐	☐
	p	Phosphor	10	15	☐	☐
		Set of 4 (Ordinary)	1·00	50	☐	☐
		Set of 4 (Phosphor)	1·00	50	☐	☐
		First Day Cover (Ordinary)		12·00	☐	
		First Day Cover (Phosphor)		12·00	☐	
		Presentation Pack (Ordinary)	9·00		☐	

England's World Cup Football Victory

1966 (18 AUG.)

700	**260**	4d multicoloured	20	20	☐	☐
		First Day Cover		6·00	☐	

261 Jodrell Bank Radio Telescope

262 British Motor cars

263 SR N6 Hovercraft

264 Windscale Reactor

British Technology

1966 (19 SEPT.)

701	**261**	4d black and lemon	15	15	☐	☐
	p	Phosphor	15	15	☐	☐
702	**262**	6d red, blue and orange	15	15	☐	☐
	p	Phosphor	15	15	☐	☐
703	**263**	1s 3d multicoloured	30	40	☐	☐
	p	Phosphor	45	50	☐	☐
704	**264**	1s 6d multicoloured	50	45	☐	☐
	p	Phosphor	65	60	☐	☐
		Set of 4 (Ordinary)	1·00	1·00	☐	☐
		Set of 4 (Phosphor)	1·25	1·25	☐	☐
		First Day Cover (Ordinary)		6·50	☐	
		First Day Cover (Phosphor)		7·00	☐	
		Presentation Pack (Ordinary)	9·00		☐	

265

266

267

268

269

270

The above show battle scenes, they were issued together *se-tenant* in horizontal strips of six within the sheet.

271 Norman Ship

272 Norman Horsemen attacking Harold's Troops

900th Anniversary of Battle of Hastings

1966 (14 OCT.) *Designs show scenes from Bayeux Tapestry.*
Wmk **179** *(sideways on 1s 3d)*

705	**265**	4d multicoloured	10	15	☐	☐
	a.	*Strip of 6*				
		Nos. 705/10	2·25	4·00	☐	☐
	p.	*Phosphor*	10	25	☐	☐
	pa	*Strip of 6*				
		Nos. 705p/10p	2·25	4·00	☐	☐
706	**266**	4d multicoloured	10	15	☐	☐
	p.	*Phosphor*	10	25	☐	☐
707	**267**	4d multicoloured	10	15	☐	☐
	p.	*Phosphor*	10	25	☐	☐

708	**268**	4d multicoloured	10	15	☐	☐
	p.	*Phosphor*	10	25	☐	☐
709	**269**	4d multicoloured	10	15	☐	☐
	p.	*Phosphor*	10	25	☐	☐
710	**270**	4d multicoloured	10	15	☐	☐
	p.	*Phosphor*	10	25	☐	☐
711	**271**	6d multicoloured	10	10	☐	☐
	p.	*Phosphor*	10	10	☐	☐
712	**272**	1s 3d multicoloured	20	20	☐	☐
	p.	*Phosphor*	20	20	☐	☐
		Set of 8 (Ordinary)	2·50	1·50	☐	☐
		Set of 8 (Phosphor)	2·50	1·90	☐	☐
		First Day Cover (Ordinary)		5·00		☐
		First Day Cover (Phosphor)		6·00		☐
		Presentation Pack (Ordinary)	10·00		☐	

273 King of the Orient

274 Snowman

Christmas

1966 (1 DEC.) *Wmk* **179** *(upright on 1s 6d)*

713	**273**	3d multicoloured	10	10	☐	☐
	p.	*Phosphor*	10	10	☐	☐
714	**274**	1s 6d multicoloured	40	40	☐	☐
	p.	*Phosphor*	40	40	☐	☐
		Set of 2 (Ordinary)	50	50	☐	☐
		Set of 2 (Phosphor)	50	50	☐	☐
		First Day Cover (Ordinary)		3·50		☐
		First Day Cover (Phosphor)		3·50		☐
		Presentation Pack (Ordinary)	10·00		☐	

275 Sea Freight

276 Air Freight

European Free Trade Association (EFTA)

1967 (20 FEB.)

715	**275**	9d multicoloured	20	20	☐	☐
	p.	*Phosphor*	20	20	☐	☐
716	**276**	1s 6d multicoloured	30	30	☐	☐
	p.	*Phosphor*	30	30	☐	☐
		Set of 2 (Ordinary)	50	50	☐	☐
		Set of 2 (Phosphor)	50	50	☐	☐
		First Day Cover (Ordinary)		3·50		☐
		First Day Cover (Phosphor)		3·75		☐
		Presentation Pack (Ordinary)	3·50		☐	

277 Hawthorn and Bramble

278 Larger Bindweed and Viper's Bugloss

279 Ox-eye Daisy, Coltsfoot and Buttercup

280 Bluebell, Red Campion and Wood Anemone

The above were issued together *se-tenant* in blocks of four within the sheet

281 Dog Violet

282 Primroses

British Wild Flowers

1967 (24 Apr.)

717	**277**	4d multicoloured	15	10 ☐	☐
	a.	Block of 4			
		Nos. 717/20	1·40	2·50 ☐	☐
	p.	Phosphor	10	10 ☐	☐
	pa.	Block of 4			
		Nos. 717p/20p	1·00	2·25 ☐	☐
718	**278**	4d multicoloured	15	10 ☐	☐
	p.	Phosphor	10	10 ☐	☐
719	**279**	4d multicoloured	15	10 ☐	☐
	p.	Phosphor	10	10 ☐	☐
720	**280**	4d multicoloured	15	10 ☐	☐
	p.	Phosphor	10	10 ☐	☐
721	**281**	9d multicoloured	15	10 ☐	☐
	p.	Phosphor	10	10 ☐	☐
722	**282**	1s 9d multicoloured	20	20 ☐	☐
	p.	Phosphor	30	20 ☐	☐
		Set of 6 (Ordinary)	1·50	65 ☐	☐
		Set of 6 (Phosphor)	1·25	65 ☐	☐
		First Day Cover (Ordinary)		5·00	☐
		First Day Cover (Phosphor)		6·00	☐
		Presentation Pack (Ordinary)	4·50		☐
		Presentation Pack (Phosphor)	4·50		☐

I   II

Two types of the 2d.

I. Value spaced away from left side of stamp.

II. Value close to left side from new multi-positive. This results in the portrait appearing in the centre, thus conforming with the other values.

1967–69 *Two phosphor bands, except where otherwise stated. No wmk.*

723	**283**	½d orange-brown	10	20 ☐	☐
724		1d olive (2 bands)	10	10 ☐	☐
725		1d olive (1 centre band)	25	30 ☐	☐
726		2d lake-brown (Type I) (2 bands)	10	15 ☐	☐
727		2d lake-brown (Type II) (2 bands)	15	15 ☐	☐
728		2d lake-brown (Type II) (1 centre band)	50	75 ☐	☐
729		3d violet (1 centre band)	10	10 ☐	☐
730		3d violet (2 bands)	30	30 ☐	☐
731		4d sepia (2 bands)	10	10 ☐	☐
732		4d olive-brown (1 centre band)	10	10 ☐	☐
733		4d vermilion (1 centre band)	10	10 ☐	☐
734		4d vermilion (1 side band)	1·75	1·50 ☐	☐
735		5d blue	10	10 ☐	☐
736		6d purple	20	20 ☐	☐
737	**284**	7d emerald	40	30 ☐	☐
738		8d vermilion	15	30 ☐	☐
739		8d turquoise-blue	55	60 ☐	☐
740		9d green	50	30 ☐	☐
741	**283**	10d drab	45	50 ☐	☐
742		1s violet	40	30 ☐	☐
743		1s 6d blue and dp blue	50	30 ☐	☐
	c.	Phosphorised paper	85	90 ☐	☐
744		1s 9d orange and black	40	30 ☐	☐
		Set of 16 (one of each value and colour)	3·00	3·25 ☐	☐
		Presentation Pack (one of each value)	6·00		☐
		Presentation Pack (German)	35·00		☐

First Day Covers

5 June 1967	Nos. 731, 742, 744	1·00	☐
8 Aug. 1967	Nos. 729, 740, 743	1·00	☐
5 Feb. 1968	Nos. 723/4, 726, 736	1·00	☐
1 July 1968	Nos. 735, 737/8, 741	1·00	☐

No. 734 exists with phosphor band at the left or right.

283 (value at left)   **284** (value at right)

285 Master Lambton
(Sir Thomas Lawrence)

286 Mares and Foals in a
Landscape (George Stubbs)

287 Children Coming Out
of School (L S Lowry)

288 Gipsy Moth IV

British Paintings

1967 (10 JULY) *Two phosphor bands. No wmk*

748	285	4d multicoloured		10	10	☐	☐
749	286	9d multicoloured		20	20	☐	☐
750	287	1s 6d multicoloured		35	25	☐	☐
		Set of 3		50	50	☐	☐
		First Day Cover			4·00		☐
		Presentation Pack		8·00			☐

Sir Francis Chichester's World Voyage

1967 (24 JULY) *Three phosphor bands. No wmk*

751	288	1s 9d multicoloured		25	25	☐	☐
		First Day Cover			2·25		☐

289 Radar Screen

290 *Penicillium notatum*

291 Vickers VC-10 Jet Engines

292 Television Equipment

British Discovery and Invention

1967 (19 SEPT.) *Two phosphor bands (except 4d, three bands). Wmk* **179** *(sideways on 1s 9d)*

752	289	4d yell, blk & verm		10	10	☐	☐
753	290	1s multicoloured		10	10	☐	☐
754	291	1s 6d multicoloured		25	15	☐	☐
755	292	1s 9d multicoloured		30	20	☐	☐
		Set of 4		60	50	☐	☐
		First Day Cover			2·50		☐
		Presentation Pack		3·00			☐

NO WATERMARK All the following issues are on un-watermarked paper unless stated.

293 The Adoration of
the Shepherds
(School of Seville)

294 Madonna and
Child (Murillo)

295 The Adoration of the Shepherds
(Louis Le Nain)

Christmas

1967 *Two phosphor bands (except 3d, one phosphor band)*

756	293	3d multicoloured (27 Nov.)		10	10	☐	☐
757	294	4d multicoloured (18 Oct.)		10	10	☐	☐
758	295	1s 6d multicoloured (27 Nov.)		35	35	☐	☐
		Set of 3		50	50	☐	☐
		First Day Covers (2)			5·00		☐

Gift Pack 1967

1967 (27 NOV.) *Comprises Nos. 715p/22p and 748/58*

	Gift Pack		2·50	☐

1967–68 *No wmk*   *Perf 11 × 12*

759	166	2s 6d brown		40	50	☐	☐
760	167	5s red		1·00	1·00	☐	☐
761	168	10s blue		5·50	7·00	☐	☐
762	169	£1 black		4·50	6·00	☐	☐
		Set of 4		10·00	13·00	☐	☐

296 Tarr Steps. Exmoor

297 Aberfeldy Bridge

298 Menai Bridge

299 M4 Viaduct

British Bridges

1968 (29 Apr.) *Two phosphor bands*

763	296	4d multicoloured		10	10	☐ ☐
764	297	9d multicoloured		10	10	☐ ☐
765	298	1s 6d multicoloured		20	15	☐ ☐
766	299	1s 9d multicoloured		25	30	☐ ☐
		Set of 4		60	60	☐ ☐
		First Day Cover			3·50	☐
		Presentation Pack		2·50		☐

300 'TUC' and Trades Unionists

301 Mrs Emmeline Pankhurst (statue)

302 Sopwith Camel and English Electric Lightning Fighters

303 Captain Cook's *Endeavour* and Signature

British Anniversaries. Events described on stamps

1968 (29 May) *Two phosphor bands*

767	300	4d multicoloured	10	10	☐ ☐
768	301	9d violet, grey and black	10	10	☐ ☐
769	302	1s multicoloured	20	20	☐ ☐
770	303	1s 9d ochre and brown	25	25	☐ ☐
		Set of 4	60	60	☐ ☐
		First Day Cover		6·50	☐
		Presentation Pack	4·00		☐

304 'Queen Elizabeth I' (Unknown Artist)

305 'Pinkie' (Lawrence)

306 'Ruins of St Mary Le Port' (Piper)

307 'The Hay Wain' (Constable)

British Paintings

1968 (12 Aug.) *Two phosphor bands*

771	304	4d multicoloured		10	10	☐ ☐
772	305	1s multicoloured		15	15	☐ ☐
773	306	1s 6d multicoloured		20	20	☐ ☐
774	307	1s 9d multicoloured		25	25	☐ ☐
		Set of 4		60	60	☐ ☐
		First Day Cover			2·75	☐
		Presentation Pack		2·25		☐
		Presentation Pack (German)		5·00		☐

Gift Pack 1968

1968 (16 Sept.) *Comprises Nos.* 763/74

Gift Pack		8·00	☐
Gift Pack (German)		18·00	☐

Collectors Pack 1968

1968 (16 Sept.) *Comprises Nos.* 752/8 *and* 763/74

Collectors Pack		8·00	☐

308 Girl and Boy with Rocking Horse

309 Girl with Doll's House

310 Boy with Train Set

Christmas

1968 (25 Nov.) *Two phosphor bands (except 4d, one centre phosphor band)*

775	**308**	4d multicoloured		10	10	☐ ☐
776	**309**	9d multicoloured		15	15	☐ ☐
777	**310**	1s 6d multicoloured		25	25	☐ ☐
	Set of 3			40	40	☐ ☐
	First Day Cover				2·25	☐
	Presentation Pack			3·75		☐
	Presentation Pack (German)			4·00		☐

311 Queen Elizabeth 2

312 Elizabethan Galleon   **313** East Indiaman

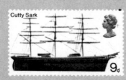

314 Cutty Sark

315 Great Britain

The 9d and 1s values were arranged in horizontal strips of three and pairs respectively throughout the sheet.

316 *Mauretania I*

British Ships

1969 (15 Jan.) *Two phosphor bands (except 5d, one hor phosphor band, 1s, two vert phosphor bands at right)*

778	**311**	5d multicoloured		10	10	☐ ☐
779	**312**	9d multicoloured		10	15	☐ ☐
		a. Strip. Nos. 779/81		1·50	1·75	☐
780	**313**	9d multicoloured		10	15	☐ ☐
781	**314**	9d multicoloured		10	15	☐ ☐
782	**315**	1s multicoloured		40	30	☐ ☐
		a. Pair. Nos. 782/3		1·25	1·50	☐
783	**316**	1s multicoloured		40	30	☐ ☐
	Set of 6			2·00	1·00	☐ ☐
	First Day Cover				5·50	☐
	Presentation Pack			4·00		☐
	Presentation Pack (German)			19·00		☐

317 Concorde in Flight

319 Concorde's Nose and Tail

318 Plan and Elevation Views

320 (See also Type **359a**)

First Flight of Concorde

1969 (3 Mar.) *Two phosphor bands*

784	**317**	4d multicoloured		10	10	☐ ☐
785	**318**	9d multicoloured		20	20	☐ ☐
786	**319**	1s 6d deep blue, grey and light blue		30	30	☐ ☐
	Set of 3			50	50	☐ ☐
	First Day Cover				3·00	☐
	Presentation Pack			3·75		☐
	Presentation Pack (German)			15·00		☐

1969 (5 Mar.) *P 12*

787	**320**	2s 6d brown		50	30	☐ ☐
788		5s lake		2·25	60	☐ ☐
789		10s ultramarine		7·00	6·00	☐ ☐
790		£1 black		3·00	1·60	☐ ☐
	Set of 4			11·50	7·50	☐ ☐
	First Day Cover				7·50	☐
	Presentation Pack			18·00		☐
	Presentation Pack (German)			38·00		☐

21 Page from the *Daily Mail*, and Vickers FB-27 Vimy Aircraft

322 Europa and C.E.P.T. Emblems

323 I.L.O. Emblem

324 Flags of N.A.T.O. Countries

325 Vickers FB-27 Vimy Aircraft and Globe showing Flight

Anniversaries. Events described on stamps

1969 (2 APR.) *Two phosphor bands*

791	321	5d multicoloured	10	10	☐	☐
792	322	9d multicoloured	20	20	☐	☐
793	323	1s claret, red and blue	20	20	☐	☐
794	324	1s 6d multicoloured	20	20	☐	☐
795	325	1s 9d olive, yellow and turquoise-green	25	25	☐	☐
		Set of 5	85	85	☐	☐
		First Day Cover		3·50		☐
		Presentation Pack	2·75		☐	
		Presentation Pack (German)	35·00		☐	

326 Durham Cathedral

327 York Minster

328 St Giles' Cathedral, Edinburgh

329 Canterbury Cathedral

The above were issued together *se-tenant* in blocks of four within the sheet.

330 St Paul's Cathedral

331 Liverpool Metropolitan Cathedral

British Architecture (Cathedrals)

1969 (28 MAY) *Two phosphor bands*

796	326	5d multicoloured	10	10	☐	☐
	a	Block of 4 Nos. 796/9	85	1·50	☐	☐
797	327	5d multicoloured	10	10	☐	☐
798	328	5d multicoloured	10	10	☐	☐
799	329	5d multicoloured	10	10	☐	☐
800	330	9d multicoloured	15	15	☐	☐
801	331	1s 6d multicoloured	15	15	☐	☐
		Set of 6	1·00	55	☐	☐
		First Day Cover		4·00		☐
		Presentation Pack	4·00		☐	
		Presentation Pack (German)	16·00		☐	

332 The King's Gate, Caernarvon Castle

333 The Eagle Tower, Caernarvon Castle

334 Queen Eleanor's Gate, Caernarvon Castle

335 Celtic Cross, Margam Abbey

The 5d values were printed *se-tenant* in strips of three throughout the sheet

336 Prince Charles

337 Mahatma Gandhi

29

Investigation columns

Investiture of H.R.H. The Prince of Wales

1969 (1 July) *Two phosphor bands*

802	**332**	5d multicoloured ..	10	10	☐	☐
		a. Strip of 3				
		Nos. 802/4 ..	70	1·25	☐	☐
803	**333**	5d multicoloured ..	10	10	☐	☐
804	**334**	5d multicoloured ..	10	10	☐	☐
805	**335**	9d multicoloured ..	20	10	☐	☐
806	**336**	1s black and gold	20	10	☐	☐
		Set of 5	1·00	45	☐	☐
		First Day Cover ..		1·50		☐
		Presentation Pack ..	1·60			☐
		Presentation Pack (German)	16·00			☐

Gandhi Centenary Year

1969 (13 Aug.) *Two phosphor bands*

807	**337**	1s 6d multicoloured ..	30	30	☐	☐
		First Day Cover		2·00		☐

Collectors Pack 1969

1969 (15 Sept.) *Comprises Nos.* 775/86 and 791/807

	Collectors Pack	20·00		☐

338 National Giro

339 Telecommunications

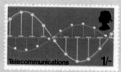

340 Telecommunications

341 Automatic Sorting

British Post Office Technology

1969 (1 Oct.) *Two phosphor bands*   Perf 13½ × 14

808	**338**	5d multicoloured ..	10	10	☐	☐
809	**339**	9d green, bl & blk..	15	15	☐	☐
810	**340**	1s green, lav & blk..	15	15	☐	☐
811	**341**	1s 6d multicoloured ..	40	40	☐	☐
		Set of 4	70	70	☐	☐
		First Day Cover ..		2·25		☐
		Presentation Pack	3·00			☐

342 Herald Angel

343 The Three Shepherds

344 The Three Kings

Christmas

1969 (26 Nov.) *Two phosphor bands* (5d, 1s 6d) *or one centre band* (4d)

812	**342**	4d multicoloured ..	10	10	☐	☐
813	**343**	5d multicoloured ..	10	10	☐	☐
814	**344**	1s 6d multicoloured ..	30	30	☐	☐
		Set of 3	45	45	☐	☐
		First Day Cover		2·50		☐
		Presentation Pack	2·50			☐

345 Fife Harling

346 Cotswold Limestone

347 Welsh Stucco

348 Ulster Thatch

British Rural Architecture

1970 (11 Feb.) *Two phosphor bands*

815	**345**	5d multicoloured ..	10	10	☐	☐
816	**346**	9d multicoloured ..	20	20	☐	☐
817	**347**	1s multicoloured ..	20	20	☐	☐
818	**348**	1s 6d multicoloured ..	35	35	☐	☐
		Set of 4	75	75	☐	☐
		First Day Cover		2·00		☐
		Presentation Pack	3·25			☐

349 Signing the Declaration of Arbroath

350 Florence Nightingale attending Patients

351 Signing of International Co-operative Alliance

352 Pilgrims and *Mayflower*

353 Sir William Herschel, Francis Baily, Sir John Herschel and Telescope

Anniversaries. *Events described on stamps*

1970 (1 APR.) *Two phosphor bands*

819	**349**	5d multicoloured	10	10	☐	☐
820	**350**	9d multicoloured	15	15	☐	☐
821	**351**	1s multicoloured	25	25	☐	☐
822	**352**	1s 6d multicoloured	30	30	☐	☐
823	**353**	1s 9d multicoloured	30	30	☐	☐
		Set of 5	1·00	1·00	☐	☐
		First Day Cover		3·50		☐
		Presentation Pack	3·25			☐

354 'Mr Pickwick and Sam' (*Pickwick Papers*)

355 'Mr and Mrs Micawber' (*David Copperfield*)

356 'David Copperfield and Betsy Trotwood' (*David Copperfield*)

357 Oliver asking for more (*Oliver Twist*)

358 'Grasmere' (from engraving by J Farrington, R.A.)

The 5d values were issued together *se-tenant* in blocks of four within the sheet.

Literary Anniversaries. *Events described on stamps*

1970 (3 JUNE) *Two phosphor bands*

824	**354**	5d multicoloured	10	10	☐	☐
	a	Block of 4				
		Nos. 824/7	1·00	1·50	☐	☐
825	**355**	5d multicoloured	10	10	☐	☐
826	**356**	5d multicoloured	10	10	☐	☐
827	**357**	5d multicoloured	10	10	☐	☐
828	**358**	1s 6d multicoloured	20	20	☐	☐
		Set of 5	1·00	55	☐	☐
		First Day Cover		3·50		☐
		Presentation Pack	3·25			☐

359

359a (Value redrawn)

Decimal Currency

1970 (17 JUNE)–**72** *10p and some printings of the 50p were issued on phosphor paper   Perf 12*

829	**359**	10p cerise	1·00	75	☐	☐
830		20p olive-green	70	15	☐	☐
831		50p ultramarine	1·50	40	☐	☐
831*b*	**359a**	£1 black	3·50	75	☐	☐
		Set of 4	6·00	1·75	☐	☐
829/31		First Day Cover		2·00		☐
831*b*		First Day Cover (6 Dec. 1972)		2·75		☐
829/31		Presentation Pack	7·50		☐	
790 (or 831*b*), 830/1		Presentation Pack	8·00			☐

360 Runners

361 Swimmers

362 Cyclists

Ninth British Commonwealth Games

1970 (15 July) *Two phosphor bands* Perf $13\frac{1}{2} \times 14$

832	**360**	5d	pink, emerald, greenish yellow & yellow-green	10	10	☐	☐
833	**361**	1s 6d	greenish blue, lilac, brown and Prussian blue	50	50	☐	☐
834	**362**	1s 9d	yellow-orange, lilac, salmon and red-brown	50	50	☐	☐
			Set of 3	1·00	1·00	☐	☐
			First Day Cover		2·00		☐
			Presentation Pack	2·75		☐	

Collectors Pack 1970

1970 (14 Sept.) *Comprises Nos.* 808/28 *and* 832/4

Collectors Pack	22·00	☐

363 1d Black (1840)
364 1s Green (1847)
365 4d Carmine (1855)

'Philympia 70' Stamp Exhibition

1970 (18 Sept.) *Two phosphor bands* Perf $14 \times 14\frac{1}{2}$

835	**363**	5d	multicoloured	10	10	☐	☐
836	**364**	9d	multicoloured	35	35	☐	☐
837	**365**	1s 6d	multicoloured	40	50	☐	☐
			Set of 3	75	90	☐	☐
			First Day Cover		2·00		☐
			Presentation Pack	2·75		☐	

366 Shepherds and Apparition of the Angel
367 Mary, Joseph, and Christ in the Manger

368 The Wise Men bearing Gifts

Christmas

1970 (25 Nov.) *Two phosphor bands* (5d, 1s 6d) *or one centre phosphor band* (4d)

838	**366**	4d	multicoloured	10	10	☐	☐
839	**367**	5d	multicoloured	10	10	☐	☐
840	**368**	1s 6d	multicoloured	35	35	☐	☐
			Set of 3	50	50	☐	☐
			First Day Cover		1·25		☐
			Presentation Pack	3·25		☐	

369   369a

Decimal Currency

1971-96. Type **369**
(a) *Printed in photogravure by Harrison & Sons (except for some ptgs of Nos.* X879 *and* X913 *which were produced by Enschedé) with phosphor bands. Perf* 15×14.

X841		$\frac{1}{2}$p turq-bl (2 bands)		10	10	☐	☐
X842		$\frac{1}{2}$p turq-bl (1 side band)		70·00	35·00	☐	☐
X843		$\frac{1}{2}$p turquoise-blue (1 centre band)		30	20	☐	☐
X844		1p crimson (2 bands)		10	10	☐	☐
X845		1p crim (1 centre band)		20	20	☐	☐
X846		1p crimson ('all-over' phosphor)		20	20	☐	☐
X847		1p crimson (1 side band)		1·00	1·25	☐	☐
X848		$1\frac{1}{2}$p black (2 bands)		20	15	☐	☐
X849		2p myr-grn (face value as in T **369**) (2 bands)		20	10	☐	☐
X850		2p myr-grn (face value as in T **369**) 'all-over' phosphor		20	15	☐	☐
X851		$2\frac{1}{2}$p mag (1 centre band)		15	10	☐	☐
X852		$2\frac{1}{2}$p magenta (1 side band)		1·25	1·75	☐	☐
X853		$2\frac{1}{2}$p magenta (2 bands)		30	75	☐	☐
X854		$2\frac{1}{2}$p rose-red (2 bands)		50	75	☐	☐
X855		3p ultramarine (2 bands)		20	10	☐	☐
X856		3p ultram (1 centre band)		20	25	☐	☐
X857		3p bright magenta (2 bands)		40	40	☐	☐
X858		$3\frac{1}{2}$p olive-grey (2 bands)		30	30	☐	☐
X859		$3\frac{1}{2}$p ol-grey (1 centre band)		30	15	☐	☐

No.	Description		
X860	3½p purple-brown (1 centre band)	1·25	1·50
X861	4p ochre-brown (2 bands)	20	20
X862	4p greenish bl (2 bands)	1·50	1·50
X863	4p greenish blue (1 centre band)	1·10	1·10
X864	4p greenish blue (1 side band)	1·50	2·00
X865	4½p grey-blue (2 bands)	20	25
X866	5p pale violet (2 bands)	20	10
X867	5p claret (1 centre band)	1·75	1·75
X868	5½p violet (2 bands)	25	25
X869	5½p violet (1 centre band)	20	20
X870	6p light emerald (2 bands)	30	15
X871	6½p greenish bl (2 bands)	45	45
X872	6½p greenish blue (1 centre band)	30	15
X873	6½p greenish blue (1 side band)	70	70
X874	7p purple-brn (2 bands)	35	25
X875	7p purple-brown (1 centre band)	35	20
X876	7p purple-brown (1 side band)	60	75
X877	7½p chestnut (2 bands)	30	25
X878	8p rosine (2 bands)	25	20
X879	8p rosine (1 centre band)	25	15
X880	8p rosine (1 side band)	80	80
X881	8½p yellowish green (2 bands)	35	20
X882	9p yellow-orange and black (2 bands)	60	30
X883	9p deep violet (2 bands)	45	25
X884	9½p purple (2 bands)	45	30
X885	10p orange-brown and chestnut (2 bands)	40	30
X886	10p orange-brn (2 bands)	40	20
X887	10p orange-brown ('all-over' phosphor)	30	45
X888	10p orange-brown (1 centre band)	30	20
X889	10p orange-brown (1 side band)	85	90
X890	10½p yellow (2 bands)	40	30
X891	10½p blue (2 bands)	70	45
X892	11p brown-red (2 bands)	60	25
X893	11½p drab (1 centre band)	45	30
X894	11½p drab (1 side band)	60	75
X895	12p yellowish green (2 bands)	60	40
X896	12p bright emerald (1 centre band)	60	40
X897	12p bright emerald (1 side band)	90	90
X898	12½p light emerald (1 centre band)	45	25
X899	12½p light emerald (1 side band)	60	60
X900	13p pale chestnut (1 centre band)	45	35
X901	13p pale chestnut (1 side band)	60	60
X902	14p grey-blue (2 bands)	1·00	45
X903	14p dp bl (1 centre band)	60	40
X904	14p dp blue (1 side band)	2·00	2·00
X905	15p brt bl (1 centre band)	50	35
X906	15p brt blue (1 side band)	2·25	2·00
X907	15½p pale violet (2 bands)	45	45
X908	16p olive-drab (2 bands)	1·25	1·25
X909	17p grey-blue (2 bands)	75	75
X910	17p dp bl (1 centre band)	1·00	1·00
X911	17p dp bl (1 side band)	1·00	1·00
X912	18p dp ol-grey (2 bands)	75	75
X913	18p bright green (1 centre band)	60	40
X914	19p bright orange-red (2 bands)	1·25	1·25
X915	20p dull purple (2 bands)	1·00	50
X916	20p brownish black (2 bands)	1·50	1·75
X917	22p bright orange-red (2 bands)	1·25	1·25
X917a	25p rose-red (2 bands)	60	60
X918	26p rosine (2 bands)	8·00	8·00
X919	31p purple (2 bands)	12·00	12·00
X920	34p ochre-brown (2 bands)	8·00	8·00
X921	50p ochre-brown (2 bands)	2·00	50
X922	50p ochre (2 bands)	3·50	3·50

(b) Printed in photogravure by Harrison and Sons on phosphorised paper. Perf 15 × 14

No.	Description		
X924	½p turquoise-blue	10	10
X925	1p crimson	10	10
X926	2p myrtle-green (face value as in T **369**)	10	10
X927	2p deep green (smaller value as in T **369a**)	10	10
X928	2p myr-grn (smaller value as in T **369a**)	1·10	1·10
X929	2½p rose-red	20	20
X930	3p bright magenta	20	20
X931	3½p purple-brown	45	45
X932	4p greenish blue	40	40
X933	4p new blue	10	10
X934	5p pale violet	30	25
X935	5p dull red-brown	10	10
X936	6p yellow-olive	25	25
X937	7p brownish red	1·75	1·75
X938	8½p yellowish green	30	55
X939	10p orange-brown	30	20
X940	10p dull orange	30	30
X941	11p brown-red	85	85
X942	11½p ochre-brown	50	45
X943	12p yellowish green	50	50
X944	13p olive-grey	60	45
X945	13½p purple-brown	65	60
X946	14p grey-blue	60	40
X947	15p ultramarine	60	40
X948	15½p pale violet	60	40
X949	16p olive-drab	60	30
X950	16½p pale chestnut	85	75
X951	17p light emerald	70	40
X952	17p grey-blue	60	40
X953	17½p pale chestnut	80	80
X954	18p deep violet	80	75
X955	18p deep olive-grey	80	60

X956	19p bright orange-red	70	50	☐ ☐
X957	19½p olive-grey	1·50	1·50	☐ ☐
X958	20p dull purple	1·00	30	☐ ☐
X959	20p turquoise-green	80	60	☐ ☐
X960	20p brownish black	70	40	☐ ☐
X961	20½p ultramarine	1·25	1·00	☐ ☐
X962	22p blue	70	45	☐ ☐
X963	22p yellow-green	70	55	☐ ☐
X964	22p bright orange-red	70	50	☐ ☐
X965	23p brown-red	1·00	60	☐ ☐
X966	23p bright green	1·00	60	☐ ☐
X967	24p violet	1·25	1·00	☐ ☐
X968	24p Indian red	1·60	1·00	☐ ☐
X969	24p chestnut	70	45	☐ ☐
X970	25p purple	1·00	1·00	☐ ☐
X971	26p rosine	90	30	☐ ☐
X972	26p drab	80	80	☐ ☐
X973	27p chestnut	1·00	1·00	☐ ☐
X974	27p violet	1·00	75	☐ ☐
X975	28p deep violet	1·00	90	☐ ☐
X976	28p ochre	1·00	90	☐ ☐
X977	28p deep bluish grey	1·00	90	☐ ☐
X978	29p ochre-brown	1·75	1·00	☐ ☐
X979	29p deep mauve	1·50	1·00	☐ ☐
X980	30p deep olive-grey	1·10	80	☐ ☐
X981	31p purple	1·00	1·25	☐ ☐
X982	31p ultramarine	1·25	1·25	☐ ☐
X983	32p greenish blue	1·00	1·00	☐ ☐
X984	33p light emerald	1·00	90	☐ ☐
X985	34p ochre-brown	1·25	90	☐ ☐
X986	34p deep bluish grey	1·50	1·25	☐ ☐
X987	34p deep mauve	1·00	80	☐ ☐
X988	35p sepia	1·25	1·00	☐ ☐
X989	35p yellow	1·25	1·00	☐ ☐
X990	37p rosine	1·50	1·50	☐ ☐
X991	39p bright mauve	1·00	1·00	☐ ☐

(c) Printed in photogravure by Harrison and Sons on ordinary paper. Perf 15 × 14

X992	50p ochre-brown	1·75	80	☐ ☐
X993	75p grey-black (smaller values as T **369**a)	2·25	2·25	☐ ☐

(d) Printed in photogravure by Harrison and Sons on ordinary paper or phosphorised paper. Perf 15 × 14

X994	50p ochre	1·50	60	☐ ☐

(e) Printed in lithography by John Waddington. Perf 14.

X996	4p greenish blue (2 bands)	20	25	☐ ☐
X997	4p greenish blue (phosphorised paper)	35	20	☐ ☐
X998	20p dull purple (2 bands)	1·10	40	☐ ☐
X999	20p dull purple (phosphorised paper)	1·40	40	☐ ☐

(f) Printed in lithography by Questa. Perf 14 (Nos X1000, X1003/4 and X1023) or 15 × 14 (others)

X1000	2p emerald-green (face value as in T **369**) (phosphorised paper)	20	20	☐ ☐
	a Perf 15 × 14	30	20	☐ ☐

X1001	2p bright grn and dp grn (smaller value as in T **369**a) (phosphorised paper)	1·00	60	☐ ☐
X1002	4p greenish blue (phosphorised paper)	60	60	☐ ☐
X1003	5p light violet (phosphorised paper)	40	20	☐ ☐
X1004	5p claret (phosphorised paper)	50	20	☐ ☐
	a Perf 15 × 14	60	40	☐ ☐
X1005	13p pale chest (1 centre band)	70	70	☐ ☐
X1006	13p pale chest (1 side band)	1·00	1·00	☐ ☐
X1007	14p dp bl (1 centre band)	1·75	1·75	☐ ☐
X1008	17p dp bl (1 centre band)	75	75	☐ ☐
X1009	18p deep olive-grey (phosphorised paper)	75	75	☐ ☐
X1010	18p dp ol-grey (2 bands)	5·00	5·00	☐ ☐
X1011	18p bright green (1 centre band)	1·25	1·25	☐ ☐
X1012	18p bright green (1 side band)	1·50	1·50	☐ ☐
X1013	19p bright orange-red (phosphorised paper)	1·75	1·75	☐ ☐
X1014	20p dull purple (phosphorised paper)	1·25	1·25	☐ ☐
X1015	22p yell-grn (2 bands)	8·00	8·00	☐ ☐
X1016	22p bright.orange-red (phosphorised paper)	1·00	1·00	☐ ☐
X1017	24p chestnut (phosphorised paper)	1·00	80	☐ ☐
X1018	24p chestnut (2 bands)	1·25	1·25	☐ ☐
X1019	33p light emerald (phosphorised paper)	1·50	1·50	☐ ☐
X1020	33p light emer (2 bands)	1·25	1·25	☐ ☐
X1021	34p ochre-brn (2 bands)	7·00	7·00	☐ ☐
X1022	39p brt mauve (2 bands)	2·00	2·00	☐ ☐
X1023	75p black (face value as T **369**) (ordinary paper)	3·25	1·75	☐ ☐
	a Perf 15 × 14	3·75	3·50	☐ ☐
X1024	75p brownish grey and black (smaller value as T **369**a) (ordinary paper)	10·00	9·00	☐ ☐

(g) Printed in lithography by Walsall. Perf 14

X1050	2p deep green (phosphorised paper)	80	90	☐ ☐
X1051	14p deep blue (1 side band)	3·00	3·00	☐ ☐
X1052	19p bright orange-red (2 bands)	1·50	1·75	☐ ☐
X1053	24p chestnut (phosphorised paper)	1·25	1·25	☐ ☐
X1054	29p deep mauve (2 bands)	5·00	5·50	☐ ☐
X1055	29p deep mauve (phosphorised paper)	6·00	6·50	☐ ☐
X1056	31p ultramarine (phosphorised paper)	1·75	2·00	☐ ☐
X1057	33p light emerald (phosphorised paper)	1·25	1·25	☐ ☐
X1058	39p bright mauve (phosphorised paper)	1·25	1·25	☐ ☐

Presentation Pack (contains ½p
(X841), 1p (X844), 1½p (X848), 2p
(X849), 2½p (X851), 3p (X855), 3½p
(X858), 4p (X861), 5p (X866), 6p
(X870), 7½p (X877), 9p (X882))   5·00   ☐

Presentation Pack ('Scandinavia 71')
(contents as above)   . .   . .   35·00   ☐

Presentation Pack (contains ½p
(X841), 1p (X844), 1½p (X848), 2p
(X849), 2½p (X851), 3p (X855 or
X856), 3½p (X858 or X859), 4p
(X861), 4½p (X865), 5p (X866), 5½p
(X868 or X869), 6p (X870), 6½p
(X871 or X872), 7p (X874), 7½p
(X877), 8p (X878), 9p (X882), 10p
(X885))   . .   . .   5·00   ☐

Presentation Pack (contains ½p
(X841), 1p (X844), 1½p (X848), 2p
(X849), 2½p (X851), 3p (X856), 5p
(X866), 6½p (X872), 7p (X874 or
X875), 7½p (X877), 8p (X878), 8½p
(X881), 9p (X883), 9½p (X884) 10p
(X886), 10½p (X890), 11p (X892)
20p (X915), 50p (X921))   . .   . .   5·00   ☐

Presentation Pack (contains 2½p
(X929), 3p (X930), 4p (X996),
10½p (X891), 11½p (X893), 11½p
(X942), 12p (X943), 13p (X944),
13½p (X945), 14p (X946), 15p
(X947), 15½p (X948), 17p (X951),
17½p (X953), 18p (X954), 22p
(X962), 25p (X970), 75p (X1023))   16·00   ☐

Presentation Pack (Contains ½p
(X924), 1p (X925), 2p (X1000), 3p
(X930), 3½p (X931), 4p (X997), 5p
(X1004), 10p (X888), 12½p
(X898), 16p (X949), 16½p (X950),
17p (X952), 20p (X999), 20½p
(X961), 23p (X965), 26p (X971),
28p (X975), 31p (X981), 50p
(X992), 75p (X1023))   . .   . .   22·00   ☐

Presentation Pack (contains ½p
(X924), 1p (X925), 2p (X1000a),
3p (X930), 4p (X997), 5p
(X1004a), 10p (X939), 13p
(X900), 16p (X949), 17p (X952),
18p (X955), 20p (X999), 22p
(X963), 24p (X967), 26p (X971),
28p (X975), 31p (X981), 34p
(X985), 50p (X992), 75p
(X1023a))   . .   . .   22·00   ☐

Presentation Pack (contains 1p
(X925), 2p (X1000a), 3p (X930),
4p (X997), 5p (X1004a), 7p
(X937), 10p (X939), 12p (X896),

13p (X900), 17p (X952), 18p
(X955), 20p (X999), 22p (X963),
24p (X971), 26p (X971), 28p
(X975), 31p (X981), 34p (X985),
50p (X992), 75p (X1023a))   . .   20·00   ☐

Presentation Pack (contains 14p
(X903), 19p (X956), 20p (X959),
23p (X966), 27p (X973), 28p
(X976), 32p (X983), 35p (X988))   10·00   ☐

Presentation Pack (contains 15p
(X905), 20p (X960), 24p (X968),
29p (X979), 30p (X980), 34p
(X986), 37p (X990)   . .   . .   9·00   ☐

Presentation Pack (contains 10p
(X940), 17p (X910), 22p (X964),
26p (X972), 27p (X974), 31p
(X982), 33p (X984)   . .   . .   7·00   ☐

Presentation Pack (contains 1p
(X925), 2p (X927), 3p (X930), 4p
(X933), 5p (X935), 10p (X940),
17p (X910), 20p (X959), 22p
(X964), 26p (X972), 27p (X974),
30p (X980), 31p (X982), 32p
(X983), 33p (X984), 37p (X990),
50p (X994), 75p (X993))   . .   . .   14·00   ☐

Presentation Pack (contains 6p
(X936), 18p (X913), 24p (X969),
28p (X977), 34p (X987), 35p
(X989), 39p (X991))   . .   . .   7·00   ☐

First Day Covers

15 Feb. 1971	½p, 1p, 1½p, 2p, 2½p, 3p, 3½p, 4p, 5p, 6p, 7½p, 9p (Nos. X841, X844, X848/9, X851, X855, X858, X861, X866, X870, X877, X882) (Covers carry "POSTING DELAYED BY THE POST OFFICE STRIKE 1971" cachet)	3·00	☐
11 Aug. 1971	10p (No. X885)	1·00	☐
24 Oct. 1973	4½p, 5½p, 8p (Nos. X865 X868, X878)	1·00	☐
4 Sept. 1974	6½p (No. X871)	1·00	☐
15 Jan. 1975	7p (No. X874)	1·00	☐
24 Sept. 1975	8½p (No. X881)	1·00	☐
25 Feb. 1976	9p, 9½p, 10p, 10½p, 11p, 20p (Nos. X883/4, X886, X890, X892, X915)	2·00	☐
2 Feb. 1977	50p (No. X921)	1·00	☐
26 April. 1978	10½p (No. X891)	1·00	☐
15 Aug. 1979	11½p, 13p, 15p (Nos. X942, X944, X947)	1·00	☐
30 Jan. 1980	4p, 12p, 13½p, 17p, 17½p, 75p (Nos. X996, X943, X945, X951, X953, X1023)	2·00	☐
22 Oct. 1980	3p, 22p, (Nos. X930, X962)	1·00	☐

14 Jan. 1981	2½p, 11½p, 14p, 15½p, 18p, 25p (Nos. X929, X893, X946, X948, X954, X970)	1·00	☐
27 Jan. 1982	5p, 12½p, 16½p, 19½p, 26p, 29p (Nos. X1004, X898, X950, X957, X971, X978)	2·00	☐
30 March 1983	3½p, 16p, 17p, 20½p, 23p, 28p, 31p (Nos. X931, X949, X952, X961, X965, X975, X981)	3·00	☐
28 Aug. 1984	13p, 18p, 22p, 24p, 34p (Nos. X900, X955, X963, X967, X985)	3·00	☐
29 Oct. 1985	7p, 12p (Nos. X937, X896)	2·00	☐
23 Aug. 1988	14p, 19p, 20p, 23p, 27p, 28p, 32p, 35p (Nos. X903, X956, X959, X966, X973, X976, X983, X988)	5·00	☐
26 Sept. 1989	15p, 20p, 24p, 29p, 30p, 34p, 37p (Nos. X905, X960, X968, X979/80, X986, X990)	4·75	☐
4 Sept. 1990	10p, 17p, 22p, 26p, 27p, 31p, 33p (Nos. X940, X910, X964, X972, X974, X982, X984)	4·50	☐
10 Sept. 1991	6p, 18p, 24p, 28p, 34p, 35p, 39p (Nos. X936, X913, X969, X977, X987, X989, X991)	5·00	☐

For similar stamps, but with elliptical perforations see Nos. Y1667/1759 in 1993.

PHOSPHOR BANDS See notes on page 15.
Phosphor bands are applied to the stamps, after the design has been printed, by a separate cylinder. On issues with "all-over" phosphor the "band" covers the entire stamp. Parts of the stamp covered by phosphor bands, or the entire surface for "all-over" phosphor versions, appear matt.
Nos. X847, X852, X864, X873, X876, X880, X889, X894, X897, X899, X901, X906, X911, X1006 and X1012 exist with the phosphor band at the left or right of the stamp.

PHOSPHORISED PAPER. First introduced as an experiment for a limited printing of the 1s 6d value (No. 743c) in 1969 this paper has the phosphor, to activate the automatic sorting machinery, added to the paper coating before the stamps were printed. Issues on this paper have a completely shiny surface. Although not adopted after this first trial further experiments on the 8½p in 1976 led to this paper being used for new printings of current values.

PRINTING PROCESSES

There is a basic distinction between stamps printed by photo gravure and those printed by lithography. Sorting the two i not as difficult as it sounds and with a little experience i should become easy to tell which method of production wa employed for a particular stamp.

The tiny dots of the printing screen give uneven edges to the values on photogravure stamps (right). Litho values have clean, clear outlines (left).

All you need is a reasonably good glass giving a magnification of ×4 or more (×10 is even better!).
The image on a photogravure stamp is created from a pattern or 'screen', of minute dots which are not evident when looking at the stamp without a glass but show up quite clearly under magnification, especially in the Queen's face and around the margin of the stamp design where it meets the white background of the paper. Now look at the value, here also, what looks to the naked eye like a straight line is in fact made up of rows of tiny little dots.
'Screens' of dots are also used in the production of litho printed stamps but they are only required where the printer is attempting to produce shades and tints as is necessary in the Queen's head portion of the stamp. Where solid colour is used, as in the background of the majority of values, there is no need to resort to a screen of dots and the background is printed as a solid mass of colour. If you look at the margins or the values of stamps produced in this way you will not see any evidence of dots—just a clear clean break between the inked portion of the stamp and the uninked white of the paper.

370 'A Mountain Road'
(T P Flanagan)

371 'Deer's Meadow'
(Tom Carr)

372 'Slieve na brock'
(Colin Middleton)

'Ulster '71' Paintings

1971 (16 June) *Two phosphor bands*

881	**370**	3p multicoloured		10	10	☐ ☐
882	**371**	7½p multicoloured		50	50	☐ ☐
883	**372**	9p multicoloured		50	50	☐ ☐
		Set of 3		1·00	1·00	☐ ☐
		First Day Cover			3·00	☐
		Presentation Pack			5·00	☐

373 John Keats
(150th Death Anniv)

374 Thomas Gray
(Death Bicentenary)

375 Sir Walter Scott
(Birth Bicentenary)

Literary Anniversaries. *Events described above*

1971 (28 July) *Two phosphor bands*

884	**373**	3p black, gold & bl		10	10	☐ ☐
885	**374**	5p blk, gold & olive		50	50	☐ ☐
886	**375**	7½p black, gold & brn		50	50	☐ ☐
		Set of 3		1·00	1·00	☐ ☐
		First Day Cover			4·00	☐
		Presentation Pack			5·00	☐

376 Servicemen and Nurse
of 1921

377 Roman Centurion

378 Rugby Football, 1871

British Anniversaries. *Events described on stamps*

1971 (25 Aug.) *Two phosphor bands*

887	**376**	3p multicoloured		10	10	☐ ☐
888	**377**	7½p multicoloured		50	50	☐ ☐
889	**378**	9p multicoloured		50	50	☐ ☐
		Set of 3		1·00	1·00	☐ ☐
		First Day Cover			3·00	☐
		Presentation Pack			5·00	☐

379 Physical Sciences Building,
University College of
Wales, Aberystwyth

380 Faraday Building,
Southampton
University

381 Engineering Department,
Leicester University

382 Hexagon Restaurant,
Essex University

British Architecture (Modern University Buildings)

1971 (22 Sept.) *Two phosphor bands*

890	**379**	3p multicoloured	10	10	☐	☐
891	**380**	5p multicoloured	20	20	☐	☐
892	**381**	7½p ochre, black and purple-brown	50	50	☐	☐
893	**382**	9p multicoloured	90	90	☐	☐
		Set of 4	1·50	1·50	☐	☐
		First Day Cover		4·00	☐	
		Presentation Pack	5·50		☐	

Collectors Pack 1971

1971 (29 Sept.) *Comprises Nos. 835/40 and 881/93*

		Collectors Pack	25·00	☐

383 Dream of the Wise Men

384 Adoration of the Magi

385 Ride of the Magi

Christmas

1971 (13 Oct.) *Two phosphor bands (3p, 7½p) or one centre phosphor band (2½p)*

894	**383**	2½p multicoloured	10	10	☐	☐
895	**384**	3p multicoloured	10	10	☐	☐
896	**385**	7½p multicoloured	90	90	☐	☐
		Set of 3	1·00	1·00	☐	☐
		First Day Cover		4·00	☐	
		Presentation Pack	4·50		☐	

386 Sir James Clark Ross

387 Sir Martin Frobisher

388 Henry Hudson

389 Capt. Robert F. Scott

British Polar Explorers

1972 (16 Feb.) *Two phosphor bands*

897	**386**	3p multicoloured	10	10	☐	☐
898	**387**	5p multicoloured	20	20	☐	☐
899	**388**	7½p multicoloured	50	50	☐	☐
900	**389**	9p multicoloured	90	90	☐	☐
		Set of 4	1·50	1·50	☐	☐
		First Day Cover		6·00	☐	
		Presentation Pack	5·00		☐	

390 Statuette of Tutankhamun

391 19th century Coastguard

392 Ralph Vaughan Williams and Score

Anniversaries. Events described on stamps

1972 (26 Apr.) *Two phosphor bands*

901	**390**	3p multicoloured	10	10	☐	☐
902	**391**	7½p multicoloured	50	50	☐	☐
903	**392**	9p multicoloured	50	50	☐	☐
		Set of 3	1·00	1·00	☐	☐
		First Day Cover		3·00	☐	
		Presentation Pack	4·50		☐	

393 St Andrew's, Greensted-juxta-Ongar, Essex

394 All Saints, Earls Barton, Northants

395 St Andrew's, Letheringsett, Norfolk

396 St Andrew's, Helpringham, Lincs

397 St Mary the Virgin, Huish Episcopi, Somerset

398 Microphones, 1924–69

399 Horn Loudspeaker

400 TV Camera, 1972

401 Oscillator and Spark Transmitter, 1897

Broadcasting Anniversaries. Events described on stamps

1972 (13 SEPT.) *Two phosphor bands*

909	**398**	3p multicoloured ..	10	10	☐	☐
910	**399**	5p multicoloured ..	15	20	☐	☐
911	**400**	7½p multicoloured ..	75	75	☐	☐
912	**401**	9p multicoloured ..	75	75	☐	☐
		Set of 4	1·50	1·50	☐	☐
		First Day Cover		4·00		☐
		Presentation Pack	3·75		☐	

402 Angel holding Trumpet

403 Angel playing Lute

British Architecture (Village Churches)

1972 (21 JUNE) *Two phosphor bands*

904	**393**	3p multicoloured ..	10	10	☐	☐
905	**394**	4p multicoloured ..	20	20	☐	☐
906	**395**	5p multicoloured ..	20	25	☐	☐
907	**396**	7½p multicoloured ..	70	80	☐	☐
908	**397**	9p multicoloured ..	75	90	☐	☐
		Set of 5	1·75	2·00	☐	☐
		First Day Cover		5·00		☐
		Presentation Pack	5·50		☐	

'Belgica '72' Souvenir Pack

1972 (24 JUNE) *Comprises Nos. 894/6 and 904/8*

	Souvenir Pack	7·00		☐

404 Angel playing Harp

Christmas

1972 (18 Oct.) *Two phosphor bands (3p, 7½p) or one centre phosphor band (2½p)*

913	**402**	2½p multicoloured	10	15	☐	☐
914	**403**	3p multicoloured	10	15	☐	☐
915	**404**	7½p multicoloured	90	80	☐	☐
		Set of 3	1·00	1·00	☐	☐
		First Day Cover		3·00	☐	
		Presentation Pack	2·75		☐	

405 Queen Elizabeth II and Prince Philip

406 Europe

Royal Silver Wedding

1972 (20 Nov.) *3p 'all-over' phosphor, 20p without phosphor*

916	**405**	3p brownish black, deep blue and silver	25	25	☐	☐
917		20p brownish black, reddish purple and silver	1·00	1·00	☐	☐
		Set of 2	1·25	1·25	☐	☐
		First Day Cover		2·00	☐	
		Presentation Pack	2·50		☐	
		Presentation Pack (Japanese)	3·50		☐	
		Souvenir Book	3·00		☐	
		Gutter Pair (3p)	1·00		☐	
		Traffic Light Gutter Pair (3p)	20·00		☐	

Collectors Pack 1972

1972 (20 Nov.) *Comprises Nos. 897/917*

	Collectors Pack	25·00	☐

Nos. 920/1 were issued horizontally *se-tenant* throughout the sheet.

Britain's Entry into European Communities

1973 (3 Jan.) *Two phosphor bands*

919	**406**	3p multicoloured	10	10	☐	☐
920		5p multicoloured (blue jigsaw)	25	50	☐	☐
		a. Pair Nos. 920/1	1·25	1·50	☐	☐
921		5p multicoloured (green jigsaw)	25	50	☐	☐
		Set of 3	1·25	1·00	☐	☐
		First Day Cover		3·50	☐	
		Presentation Pack	2·50		☐	

407 Oak Tree

British Trees (1st issue)

1973 (28 Feb.) *Two phosphor bands*

922	**407**	9p multicoloured	50	50	☐	☐
		First Day Cover		2·50		☐
		Presentation Pack	2·50		☐	

See also No. 949

408 David Livingstone

409 H. M. Stanley

The above were issued horizontally *se-tenant* throughout the sheet.

410 Sir Francis Drake

411 Sir Walter Raleigh

412 Charles Sturt

British Explorers

1973 (18 APR.) 'All-over' phosphor

923	408	3p multicoloured	25	20	☐	☐
		a. Pair. Nos. 923/4	1·00	1·25	☐	☐
924	409	3p multicoloured	25	20	☐	☐
925	410	5p multicoloured	20	30	☐	☐
926	411	7½p multicoloured	20	30	☐	☐
927	412	9p multicoloured	25	40	☐	☐
		Set of 5	1·50	2·00	☐	☐
		First Day Cover		4·50		☐
		Presentation Pack	3·50		☐	

413

414

415

County Cricket 1873–1973

1973 (16 MAY) Designs show sketches of W. G. Grace by Harry Furniss. Queen's head in gold 'All-over' phosphor

928	413	3p black and brown	10	10	☐	☐
929	414	7½p black and green	80	70	☐	☐
930	415	9p black and blue	1·00	90	☐	☐
		Set of 3	1·75	1·50	☐	☐
		First Day Cover		3·50		☐
		Presentation Pack	3·50		☐	
		Souvenir Book	6·25		☐	
		PHQ Card (No. 928)	48·00	£140	☐	☐

The PHQ Card did not become available until mid-July. The used price quoted is for an example used in July or August 1973.

416 'Self-portrait' (Sir Joshua Reynolds)

417 'Self-portrait' (Sir Henry Raeburn)

418 'Nelly O'Brien' (Sir Joshua Reynolds)

419 'Rev R. Walker (The Skater)' (Sir Henry Raeburn)

Artistic Anniversaries. Events described on stamps

1973 (4 JULY) 'All-over' phosphor

931	416	3p multicoloured	10	10	☐	☐
932	417	5p multicoloured	20	25	☐	☐
933	418	7½p multicoloured	55	50	☐	☐
934	419	9p multicoloured	60	60	☐	☐
		Set of 4	1·25	1·25	☐	☐
		First Day Cover		2·75		☐
		Presentation Pack	2·75		☐	

420 Court Masque Costumes

421 St Paul's Church, Covent Garden

422 Prince's Lodging. Newmarket

423 Court Masque Stage Scene

42

The 3p and 5p values were printed horizontally *se-tenant* within the sheet

400th Anniversary of the Birth of Inigo Jones

1973 (15 AUG.) *'All-over' phosphor*

935	**420**	3p	deep mauve, black and gold	10	15	☐ ☐
	a	*Pair. Nos. 935/6*		35	40	☐ ☐
936	**421**	3p	deep brown, black and gold	10	15	☐ ☐
937	**422**	5p	blue, black and gold	40	45	☐ ☐
	a	*Pair. Nos. 937/8*		1·50	1·50	☐ ☐
938	**423**	5p	grey-olive, black and gold	40	45	☐ ☐
		Set of 4		1·60	1·10	☐ ☐
		First Day Cover			2·75	☐
		Presentation Pack		3·75		☐
		PHQ Card (*No.* 936)		£120	95·00	☐ ☐

424 Palace of Westminster seen from Whitehall

425 Palace of Westminster seen from Millbank

19th Commonwealth Parliamentary Conference

1973 (12 SEPT.) *'All-over' phosphor*

939	**424**	8p	black, grey and pale buff	50	60	☐ ☐
940	**425**	10p	gold and black	50	40	☐ ☐
		Set of 2		1·00	1·00	☐ ☐
		First Day Cover			2·50	☐
		Presentation Pack		2·50		☐
		Souvenir Book		5·00		☐
		PHQ Card (*No.* 939)		40·00	90·00	☐ ☐

426 Princess Anne and Captain Mark Phillips

Royal Wedding

1973 (14 Nov.) *'All-over' phosphor*

941	**426**	3½p	violet and silver	10	10	☐ ☐
942		20p	brown and silver	90	90	☐ ☐
		Set of 2		1·00	1·00	☐ ☐
		First Day Cover			2·50	☐
		Presentation Pack		2·50		☐
		PHQ Card (*No.* 941)		7·50	20·00	☐ ☐
		Set of 2 Gutter Pairs		4·00		☐
		Set of 2 Traffic Light Gutter Pairs		95·00		☐

427

428

429

430

431

432 'Good King Wenceslas, the Page and Peasant'

The 3p values depict the carol 'Good King Wenceslas' and were printed horizontally *se-tenant* within the sheet.

Christmas

1973 (28 Nov.) *One phosphor band* (3p) *or 'all-over' phosphor* (3½p)

943	**427**	3p	multicoloured	15	15	☐ ☐
	a	*Strip of 5. Nos. 943/7*		2·75	3·00	☐ ☐
944	**428**	3p	multicoloured	15	15	☐ ☐
945	**429**	3p	multicoloured	15	15	☐ ☐
946	**430**	3p	multicoloured	15	15	☐ ☐
947	**431**	3p	multicoloured	15	15	☐ ☐
948	**432**	3½p	multicoloured	15	15	☐ ☐
		Set of 6		2·75	80	☐ ☐
		First Day Cover			3·50	☐
		Presentation Pack		3·25		☐

Collectors Pack 1973

1973 (28 Nov.) *Comprises Nos.* 919/48

	Collectors Pack	23·00	☐

433 Horse Chestnut

British Trees (2nd issue)

1974 (27 FEB.) 'All-over' phosphor

949	**433**	10p multicoloured	50	50	☐	☐
		First Day Cover		2·50		☐
		Presentation Pack	2·25		☐	
		PHQ Card	£110	70·00	☐	☐
		Gutter Pair	3·00		☐	
		Traffic Light Gutter Pair	60·00		☐	

434 First Motor Fire-engine, 1904

435 Prize-winning Fire-engine, 1863

436 Steam Fire-engine, 1830

437 Fire-engine, 1766

200th Anniversary of Public Fire Services

1974 (24 APR.) 'All-over' phosphor

950	**434**	3½p multicoloured	10	10	☐	☐
951	**435**	5½p multicoloured	25	25	☐	☐
952	**436**	8p multicoloured	35	35	☐	☐
953	**437**	10p multicoloured	40	40	☐	☐
		Set of 4	1·00	1·00	☐	☐
		First Day Cover		3·50		☐
		Presentation Pack	3·00		☐	
		PHQ Card (No. 950)	£120	70·00	☐	☐
		Set of 4 Gutter Pairs	4·00		☐	
		Set of 4 Traffic Light Gutter Pairs	60·00		☐	

438 P & O Packet Peninsular, 1888

439 Farman H.F. III Biplane, 1911

440 Airmail-blue Van and Postbox, 1930

441 Imperial Airways Short S.21 Flying Boat Maia, 1937

Centenary of Universal Postal Union

1974 (12 JUNE) 'All-over' phosphor

954	**438**	3½p multicoloured	10	10	☐	☐
955	**439**	5½p multicoloured	20	25	☐	☐
956	**440**	8p multicoloured	30	35	☐	☐
957	**441**	10p multicoloured	50	40	☐	☐
		Set of 4	1·00	1·00	☐	☐
		First Day Cover		2·50		☐
		Presentation Pack	2·00		☐	
		Set of 4 Gutter Pairs	4·00		☐	
		Set of 4 Traffic Light Gutter Pairs	45·00		☐	

442 Robert the Bruce

443 Owain Glyndŵr

444 Henry the Fifth

445 The Black Prince

Medieval Warriors

1974 (10 JULY) 'All-over' phosphor

958	**442**	4½p multicoloured	10	10	☐	☐
959	**443**	5½p multicoloured	20	20	☐	☐
960	**444**	8p multicoloured	50	40	☐	☐
961	**445**	10p multicoloured	55	40	☐	☐
		Set of 4	1·25	1·00	☐	☐
		First Day Cover		3·50		☐
		Presentation Pack	4·00		☐	
		PHQ Cards (set of 4)	30·00	22·00	☐	☐
		Set of 4 Gutter Pairs	6·00		☐	
		Set of 4 Traffic Light Gutter Pairs	65·00		☐	

446 Churchill in Royal Yacht Squadron Uniform

447 Prime Minister, 1940

448 Secretary for War and Air 1919

449 War Correspondent. South Africa. 1899

Birth Centenary of Sir Winston Churchill

1974 (9 Oct.) *Queen's head and inscription in silver 'All-over' phosphor*

962	**446**	4½p green and blue	15	15	☐	☐
963	**447**	5½p grey and black	30	25	☐	☐
964	**448**	8p rose and lake	60	50	☐	☐
965	**449**	10p stone and brown	65	50	☐	☐
		Set of 4	1·50	1·50	☐	☐
		First Day Cover		3·50	☐	
		Presentation Pack	2·00		☐	
		Souvenir Book	2·75		☐	
		PHQ Card (No. 963)	6·00	12·00	☐	☐
		Set of 4 Gutter Pairs	4·50		☐	
		Set of 4 Traffic Light Gutter Pairs	40·00		☐	

450 Adoration of the Magi (York Minster. *c* 1355)

451 The Nativity (St Helen's Church. Norwich. *c* 1480)

452 Virgin and Child (Ottery St Mary Church. *c* 1350)

453 Virgin and Child (Worcester Cathedral *c* 1224)

Christmas

1974 (27 Nov.) *Designs show church roof bosses. One phosphor band (3½p) or 'all-over' phosphor (others)*

966	**450**	3½p multicoloured	10	10	☐	☐
967	**451**	4½p multicoloured	10	10	☐	☐
968	**452**	8p multicoloured	45	45	☐	☐
969	**453**	10p multicoloured	50	50	☐	☐
		Set of 4	1·00	1·00	☐	☐
		First Day Cover		2·50	☐	
		Presentation Pack	1·75		☐	
		Set of 4 Gutter Pairs	4·00		☐	
		Set of 4 Traffic Light Gutter Pairs	40·00		☐	

Collectors Pack 1974

1974 (27 Nov.) *Comprises Nos 949-69*

	Collectors Pack	8·50	☐

454 Invalid in Wheelchair

Health and Handicap Funds

1975 (22 Jan.) *'All-over' phosphor*

970	**454**	4½p · 1½p azure and blue	25	25	☐	☐
		First Day Cover		1·25		☐
		Gutter Pair	50		☐	
		Traffic Light Gutter Pair	1·00		☐	

455 'Peace – Burial at Sea'

456 'Snowstorm – Steamer off a Harbour's Mouth'

457 The Arsenal. Venice

458 St Laurent

Birth Bicentenary of J. M. W. Turner

1975 (19 Feb.) *'All-over' phosphor*

971	**455**	4½p multicoloured	10	10	☐	☐
972	**456**	5½p multicoloured	15	15	☐	☐
973	**457**	8p multicoloured	40	40	☐	☐
974	**458**	10p multicoloured	45	45	☐	☐
		Set of 4	1·00	1·00	☐	☐
		First Day Cover		3·00		☐
		Presentation Pack	2·50		☐	
		PHQ Card (No 972)	35·00	11·00	☐	☐
		Set of 4 Gutter Pairs	2·50		☐	
		Set of 4 Traffic Light Gutter Pairs	7·00		☐	

459 Charlotte Square,
Edinburgh

460 The Rows, Chester

The above were printed horizontally *se-tenant* throughout the sheet.

461 Royal Observatory,
Greenwich

462 St George's
Chapel, Windsor

463 National Theatre, London

European Architectural Heritage Year
1975 (23 APR.) *'All-over' phosphor*

975	**459**	7p multicoloured	..	30	30	☐	☐
		a. *Pair. Nos.* 975/6		80	90	☐	☐
976	**460**	7p multicoloured	..	30	30	☐	☐
977	**461**	8p multicoloured	..	20	25	☐	☐
978	**462**	10p multicoloured	..	20	25	☐	☐
979	**463**	12p multicoloured	..	20	35	☐	☐
		Set of 5		1·25	1·25	☐	☐
		First Day Cover			4·25	☐	
		Presentation Pack		3·50		☐	
		PHQ Cards (Nos. 975/7)	.	8·00	11·00	☐	☐
		Set of 5 Gutter Pairs ..		4·00		☐	
		Set of 5 Traffic Light Gutter Pairs		16·00		☐	

464 Sailing Dinghies

465 Racing Keel Boats

466 Cruising Yachts

467 Multihulls

Sailing
1975 (11 JUNE) *'All-over' phosphor*

980	**464**	7p multicoloured	..	20	20	☐	☐
981	**465**	8p multicoloured	..	35	30	☐	☐
982	**466**	10p multicoloured	..	40	30	☐	☐
983	**467**	12p multicoloured	..	45	35	☐	☐
		Set of 4 ..		1·25	1·00	☐	☐
		First Day Cover ..			2·50	☐	
		Presentation Pack		1·50		☐	
		PHQ Card (No. 981)		4·50	10·00	☐	☐
		Set of 4 Gutter Pairs		2·50		☐	
		Set of 4 Traffic Light Gutter Pairs ..		24·00		☐	

1825 Stockton and Darlington Railway

468 Stephenson's
Locomotion, 1825

1876 North British Railway Drummond

469 *Abbotsford,*
1876

1923 Great Western Railway Castle Class

470 *Caerphilly Castle,* 1923

1975 British Rail Inter-City Service HST

471 High Speed Train, 1975

150th Anniversary of Public Railways
1975 (13 AUG.) *'All-over' phosphor*

984	**468**	7p multicoloured	..	20	20	☐	☐
985	**469**	8p multicoloured	..	45	35	☐	☐
986	**470**	10p multicoloured	..	50	40	☐	☐
987	**471**	12p multicoloured	..	55	45	☐	☐
		Set of 4		1·50	1·25	☐	☐
		First Day Cover			3·50	☐	
		Presentation Pack ..		2·75		☐	
		Souvenir Book		3·00		☐	
		PHQ Cards (set of 4) ..		55·00	22·00	☐	☐
		Set of 4 Gutter Pairs ..		3·00		☐	
		Set of 4 Traffic Light Gutter Pairs		11·00		☐	

472 Palace of Westminster

62nd Inter-Parliamentary Union Conference

1975 (3 Sept) *All-over phosphor*

988	**472**	12p multicoloured	50	50	☐	☐
		First Day Cover		1·25		☐
		Presentation Pack	1·25		☐	
		Gutter Pair	1·00		☐	
		Traffic Light Gutter Pair	3·00		☐	

473 Emma and Mr Woodhouse (*Emma*)

474 Catherine Morland (*Northanger Abbey*)

475 Mr Darcy (*Pride and Prejudice*)

476 Mary and Henry Crawford (*Mansfield Park*)

Birth Bicentenary of Jane Austen (Novelist)

1975 (22 Oct) *'All-over' phosphor*

989	**473**	8½p multicoloured	20	20	☐	☐
990	**474**	10p multicoloured	25	25	☐	☐
991	**475**	11p multicoloured	30	30	☐	☐
992	**476**	13p multicoloured	35	35	☐	☐
		Set of 4	1·00	1·00	☐	☐
		First Day Cover		2·50		☐
		Presentation Pack	2·25		☐	
		PHQ Cards (set of 4)	20·00	16·00	☐	☐
		Set of 4 Gutter Pairs	2·50		☐	
		Set of 4 Traffic Light Gutter Pairs	7·00		☐	

477 Angels with Harp and Lute

478 Angel with Mandolin

479 Angel with Horn

480 Angel with Trumpet

Christmas

1975 (26 Nov) *One phosphor band (6½p) phosphor-inked (8½p) (background) or 'all-over' phosphor (others)*

993	**477**	6½p multicoloured	20	15	☐	☐
994	**478**	8½p multicoloured	20	20	☐	☐
995	**479**	11p multicoloured	30	35	☐	☐
996	**480**	13p multicoloured	40	40	☐	☐
		Set of 4	1·00	1·00	☐	☐
		First Day Cover		2·50		☐
		Presentation Pack	2·00		☐	
		Set of 4 Gutter Pairs	2·50		☐	
		Set of 4 Traffic Light Gutter Pairs	7·00		☐	

Collectors Pack 1975

1975 (26 Nov) *Comprises Nos 970/96*

	Collectors Pack	7·50	☐

481 Housewife

482 Policeman

483 District Nurse

484 Industrialist

Telephone Centenary

1976 (10 Mar.) 'All-over' phosphor

997	**481**	8½p multicoloured	20	20	☐	☐
998	**482**	10p multicoloured	25	25	☐	☐
999	**483**	11p multicoloured	30	30	☐	☐
1000	**484**	13p multicoloured	35	35	☐	☐
		Set of 4	1·00	1·00	☐	☐
		First Day Cover		2·50		☐
		Presentation Pack	2·00		☐	
		Set of 4 Gutter Pairs	2·50		☐	
		Set of 4 Traffic Light Gutter Pairs	7·00		☐	

485 Hewing Coal
(Thomas Hepburn)

486 Machinery
(Robert Owen)

487 Chimney Cleaning
(Lord Shaftesbury)

488 Hands clutching Prison
Bars (Elizabeth Fry)

Social Reformers

1976 (28 Apr.) 'All-over' phosphor

1001	**485**	8½p multicoloured	20	20	☐	☐
1002	**486**	10p multicoloured	25	25	☐	☐
1003	**487**	11p black, slate-grey and drab	30	30	☐	☐
1004	**488**	13p slate-grey, black and green	35	35	☐	☐
		Set of 4	1·00	1·00	☐	☐
		First Day Cover		2·50		☐
		Presentation Pack	2·25		☐	
		PHQ Card (No. 1001)	5·00	7·50	☐	☐
		Set of 4 Gutter Pairs	2·50		☐	
		Set of 4 Traffic Light Gutter Pairs	7·00		☐	

489 Benjamin Franklin (bust by
Jean Jacques Caffieri)

Bicentenary of American Independence

1976 (2 June) 'All-over' phosphor

1005	**489**	11p multicoloured	50	50	☐	☐
		First Day Cover		1·50		☐
		Presentation Pack	1·25		☐	
		PHQ Card	3·00	8·50	☐	☐
		Gutter Pair	1·00		☐	
		Traffic Light Gutter Pair	2·00		☐	

490 'Elizabeth of Glamis'

491 'Grandpa Dickson'

492 'Rosa Mundi'

493 'Sweet Briar'

Centenary of Royal National Rose Society

1976 (30 June) 'All-over' phosphor

1006	**490**	8½p multicoloured	20	20	☐	☐
1007	**491**	10p multicoloured	30	30	☐	☐
1008	**492**	11p multicoloured	55	50	☐	☐
1009	**493**	13p multicoloured	60	40	☐	☐
		Set of 4	1·50	1·25	☐	☐
		First Day Cover		2·50		☐
		Presentation Pack	2·25		☐	
		PHQ Cards (set of 4)	28·00	11·00	☐	☐
		Set of 4 Gutter Pairs	3·00		☐	
		Set of 4 Traffic Light Gutter Pairs	9·00		☐	

494 Archdruid

495 Morris Dancing

Highland Gathering
Na Geamannan

496 Scots Piper

1176 1176

Eisteddfod Genedlaethol Frenhnol Cymru
Royal National Eisteddfod of Wales

497 Welsh Harpist

British Cultural Traditions

1976 (4 Aug.) 'All-over' phosphor

010	**494**	8½p multicoloured	20	20	☐	☐
011	**495**	10p multicoloured	25	25	☐	☐
012	**496**	11p multicoloured	30	30	☐	☐
013	**497**	13p multicoloured	35	35	☐	☐
		Set of 4	1·00	1·00	☐	☐
		First Day Cover		2·50	☐	
		Presentation Pack	2·00		☐	
		PHQ Cards (set of 4)	14·00	10·00	☐	☐
		Set of 4 Gutter Pairs	2·50		☐	
		Set of 4 Traffic Light Gutter Pairs	8·50		☐	

502 Virgin and Child

503 Angel with Crown

504 Angel appearing to Shepherds

505 The Three Kings

Christmas

1976 (24 Nov.) *Designs show English mediaeval embroidery. One phosphor band (6½p) or 'all-over' phosphor (others)*

1018	**502**	6½p multicoloured	15	15	☐	☐
1019	**503**	8½p multicoloured	20	20	☐	☐
1020	**504**	11p multicoloured	35	35	☐	☐
1021	**505**	13p multicoloured	40	40	☐	☐
		Set of 4	1·00	1·00	☐	☐
		First Day Cover		2·50		☐
		Presentation Pack	2·25		☐	
		PHQ Cards (set of 4)	3·00	8·00	☐	☐
		Set of 4 Gutter Pairs	2·50		☐	
		Set of 4 Traffic Light Gutter Pairs	6·50		☐	

Collectors Pack 1976

1976 (24 Nov.) Comprises Nos. 997/1021

Collectors Pack	10·00		☐

William Caxton 1476

498 The Canterbury Tales

William Caxton 1476

499 The Tretyse of Love

William Caxton 1476

500 Game and Playe of Chesse

William Caxton 1476

501 Early Printing Press

500th Anniversary of British Printing

1976 (29 Sept.) 'All-over' phosphor

1014	**498**	8½p blk, bl & gold	20	20	☐	☐
1015	**499**	10p blk, olive-grn & gold	25	25	☐	☐
1016	**500**	11p blk, grey & gold	30	30	☐	☐
1017	**501**	13p brn, ochre & gold	35	35	☐	☐
		Set of 4	1·00	1·00	☐	☐
		First Day Cover		2·50		☐
		Presentation Pack	2·50		☐	
		PHQ Cards (set of 4)	10·00	10·00	☐	☐
		Set of 4 Gutter Pairs	2·50		☐	
		Set of 4 Traffic Light Gutter Pairs	7·00		☐	

506 Lawn Tennis

507 Table Tennis

508 Squash

509 Badminton

Racket Sports

1977 (12 Jan.) *Phosphorised paper*

1022	**506**	8½p multicoloured	20	20	☐	☐
1023	**507**	10p multicoloured	35	25	☐	☐
1024	**508**	11p multicoloured	40	30	☐	☐
1025	**509**	13p multicoloured	45	35	☐	☐
		Set of 4	1·25	1·00	☐	☐
		First Day Cover		2·50		☐
		Presentation Pack	2·00		☐	
		PHQ Cards (set of 4)	6·00	9·50	☐	☐
		Set of 4 Gutter Pairs	2·50		☐	
		Set of 4 Traffic Light Gutter Pairs	6·50		☐	

510

1977 (2 Feb.)-**87** *Type* **510** *Ordinary paper*

1026	£1 green and olive	3·00	20	☐	☐
1026*b*	£1·30 drab & dp grnish bl	5·50	5·00	☐	☐
1026*c*	£1·33 pale mve & grey-blk	6·00	6·00	☐	☐
1026*d*	£1·41 drab & dp grnish bl	7·00	6·00	☐	☐
1026*e*	£1·50 pale mve & grey-blk	5·50	4·00	☐	☐
1026*f*	£1·60 drab and dp grnish bl	5·50	6·00	☐	☐
1027	£2 green and brown	5·50	75	☐	☐
1028	£5 pink and blue	13·00	2·00	☐	☐
	Presentation Pack (Nos. 1026, 1027/8)	22·00		☐	·
	Presentation Pack (No. 1026*f*)	13·00		☐	
	Set of 8 Gutter Pairs	£100		☐	
	Set of 8 Traffic Light Gutter Pairs	£150		☐	

First Day Covers

2 Feb. 1977	Nos: 1026, 1027/8	8·00	☐	
3 Aug. 1983	No. 1026*b*	5·50	☐	
28 Aug. 1984	No. 1026*c*	6·00	☐	
17 Sept. 1985	No. 1026*d*	6·00	☐	
2 Sept. 1986	No. 1026*e*	4·00	☐	
15 Sept. 1987	No. 1026*f*	6·00	☐	

511 Steroids – Conformational Analysis

512 Vitamin C – Synthesis

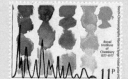

513 Starch – Chromatography

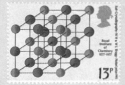

514 Salt – Crystallography

Centenary of Royal Institute of Chemistry

1977 (2 Mar.) *'All-over' phosphor*

1029	**511**	8½p multicoloured	20	20	☐	☐
1030	**512**	10p multicoloured	30	30	☐	☐
1031	**513**	11p multicoloured	30	30	☐	☐
1032	**514**	13p multicoloured	30	30	☐	☐
		Set of 4	1·00	1·00	☐	☐
		First Day Cover		2·50		☐
		Presentation Pack	2·50		☐	
		PHQ Cards (set of 4)	7·00	10·00	☐	☐
		Set of 4 Gutter Pairs	2·50		☐	
		Set of 4 Traffic Light Gutter Pairs	6·00		☐	

515

Silver Jubilee

1977 (11 May-15 June) *'All-over' phosphor*

1033	**515**	8½p multicoloured	20	20	☐	☐
1034		9p mult (15 June)	25	25	☐	☐
1035		10p multicoloured	25	25	☐	☐
1036		11p multicoloured	30	30	☐	☐
1037		13p multicoloured	40	40	☐	☐
		Set of 5	1·25	1·25	☐	☐
		First Day Covers (2)		3·50		☐
		Presentation Pack (ex 9p)	2·00		☐	
		Souvenir Book (ex 9p)	4·00		☐	
		PHQ Cards (set of 5)	9·50	9·00	☐	☐
		Set of 5 Gutter Pairs	2·75		☐	
		Set of 5 Traffic Light Gutter Pairs	4·50		☐	

519 'Gathering of Nations'

Commonwealth Heads of Government Meeting, London

1977 (8 JUNE) 'All-over' phosphor

1038 **519**	13p black, deep green rose and silver		50	50	☐	☐
	First Day Cover			1·50		☐
	Presentation Pack		1·00		☐	
	PHQ Card		2·25	4·50	☐	☐
	Gutter Pair		1·00		☐	
	Traffic Light Gutter Pair		1·25		☐	

520 Hedgehog

521 Brown Hare

522 Red Squirrel

523 Otter

524 Badger

T **520/4** were printed together, se-tenant, throughout the sheet

British Wildlife

1977 (5 OCT) 'All-over' phosphor

1039 **520**	9p multicoloured	25	20	☐	☐
	a Strip of 5				
	Nos. 1039/43	1·75	2·00	☐	☐
1040 **521**	9p multicoloured	25	20	☐	☐
1041 **522**	9p multicoloured	25	20	☐	☐
1042 **523**	9p multicoloured	25	20	☐	☐
1043 **524**	9p multicoloured	25	20	☐	☐
	Set of 5	1·75	1·00	☐	☐
	First Day Cover		2·75		☐
	Presentation Pack	2·50		☐	
	PHQ Cards (set of 5)	4·00	5·00	☐	☐
	Gutter Strip of 10	3·75		☐	
	Traffic Light Gutter Strip of 10	4·00		☐	

525 Three French Hens, Two Turtle Doves and a Partridge in a Pear Tree'

526 Six Geese a-laying, Five Gold Rings, Four Colly Birds'

527 Eight Maids a-milking, Seven Swans a-swimming'

528 Ten Pipers piping, Nine Drummers drumming'

529 Twelve Lords a-leaping, Eleven Ladies dancing'

530 A Partridge in a Pear Tree'

T **525/30** depict the carol 'The Twelve Days of Christmas'. T **525/29** were printed horizontally se-tenant throughout the sheet

Christmas

1977 (23 Nov.) One centre phosphor band (7p) or 'all-over' phosphor (9p)

1044 **525**	7p multicoloured	15	15	☐	☐
	a Strip of 5				
	Nos. 1044/8	1·00	1·50	☐	☐
1045 **526**	7p multicoloured	15	15	☐	☐
1046 **527**	7p multicoloured	15	15	☐	☐
1047 **528**	7p multicoloured	15	15	☐	☐
1048 **529**	7p multicoloured	15	15	☐	☐
1049 **530**	9p multicoloured	20	20	☐	☐
	Set of 6	1·00	85	☐	☐
	First Day Cover		2·50		☐
	Presentation Pack	2·25		☐	
	PHQ Cards (set of 6)	3·25	4·00	☐	☐
	Set of 6 Gutter Pairs	2·50		☐	
	Set of 6 Traffic Light Gutter Pairs	4·50		☐	

Collectors Pack 1977

1977 (23 Nov.) Comprises Nos. 1022/5 1029/49

	Collectors Pack	6·50	☐

531 Oil—North Sea Production Platform

532 Coal—Modern Pithead

533 Natural Gas—Flame Rising from Sea

534 Electricity—Nuclear Power Station and Uranium Atom

Energy Resources

1978 (25 Jan.) *'All-over' phosphor*

1050	**531**	9p multicoloured	..	25	20	☐	☐
1051	**532**	10½p multicoloured	..	25	30	☐	☐
1052	**533**	11p multicoloured	..	30	30	☐	☐
1053	**534**	13p multicoloured	..	30	30	☐	☐
		Set of 4	.. .. ..	1·00	1·00	☐	☐
		First Day Cover ..	.. ..		1·50		☐
		Presentation Pack	.. ..	2·00		☐	
		PHQ Cards (set of 4) ..	..	3·00	4·00	☐	☐
		Set of 4 Gutter Pairs	..	2·50		☐	
		Set of 4 Traffic Light					
		Gutter Pairs	.. ..	4·00		☐	

535 Tower of London

536 Holyroodhouse

537 Caernarvon Castle

538 Hampton Court Palace

British Architecture (Historic Buildings)

1978 (1 Mar.) *'All-over' phosphor*

1054	**535**	9p multicoloured		25	20	☐	☐
1055	**536**	10½p. multicoloured		25	30	☐	☐
1056	**537**	11p multicoloured	..	30	30	☐	☐
1057	**538**	13p multicoloured	..	30	30	☐	☐
		Set of 4	.. .. ..	1·00	1·00	☐	☐
		First Day Cover ..	..		1·50		☐
		Presentation Pack	.. ..	2·00		☐	
		PHQ Cards (set of 4) ..		2·50	4·00	☐	☐
		Set of 4 Gutter Pairs	..	2·50	-	☐	
		Set of 4 Traffic Light					
		Gutter Pairs	.. ..	4·00		☐	
MS1058		121×90 mm. Nos. 1054/57	1·25	1·50	☐	☐
		First Day Cover	.. ..		2·50		☐

No. **MS**1058 was sold at 53½p, the premium being used for the London 1980 Stamp Exhibition.

539 State Coach

540 St Edward's Crown

541 The Sovereign's Orb

542 Imperial State Crown

25th Anniversary of Coronation

1978 (31 May) *'All-over' phosphor*

1059	**539**	9p gold and blue	..	20	20	☐	☐
1060	**540**	10½p gold and red	..	25	30	☐	☐
1061	**541**	11p gold and green	..	30	30	☐	☐
1062	**542**	13p gold and violet ..		35	30	☐	☐
		Set of 4	.. ..	1·00	1·00	☐	☐
		First Day Cover ..	..		1·50		☐
		Presentation Pack	.. ..	2·25		☐	
		Souvenir Book	.. ..	4·00		☐	
		PHQ Cards (set of 4) ..		2·50	4·00	☐	☐
		Set of 4 Gutter Pairs	..	2·50		☐	
		Set of 4 Traffic Light					
		Gutter Pairs	.. ..	4·00		☐	

543 Shire Horse

544 Shetland Pony

545 Welsh Pony

546 Thoroughbred

Horses

1978 (5 July) 'All-over' phosphor

1063	**543**	9p multicoloured		20	20	☐	☐
1064	**544**	10½p multicoloured		35	25	☐	☐
1065	**545**	11p multicoloured		40	30	☐	☐
1066	**546**	13p multicoloured		45	35	☐	☐
	Set of 4			1·25	1·00	☐	☐
	First Day Cover				1·50		☐
	Presentation Pack			2·25		☐	
	PHQ Cards (set of 4)			2·50	5·00	☐	☐
	Set of 4 Gutter Pairs			2·50		☐	
	Set of 4 Traffic Light						
	Gutter Pairs			4·00		☐	

547 Penny-farthing and 1884
Safety Bicycle

548 1920 Touring Bicycles

549 Modern Small-wheel
Bicycles

550 1978 Road-racers

Centenaries of Cyclists Touring Club and British Cycling Federation

1978 (2 Aug) 'All-over' phosphor

1067	**547**	9p multicoloured		20	20	☐	☐
1068	**548**	10½p multicoloured		25	25	☐	☐
1069	**549**	11p multicoloured		30	30	☐	☐
1070	**550**	13p multicoloured		35	35	☐	☐
	Set of 4			1·00	1·00	☐	☐
	First Day Cover				1·50		☐
	Presentation Pack			2·00		☐	
	PHQ Cards (set of 4)			1·50	3·25	☐	☐
	Set of 4 Gutter Pairs			2·50		☐	
	Set of 4 Traffic Light						
	Gutter Pairs			4·00		☐	

551 Singing Carols round the
Christmas Tree

552 The Waits

553 18th-Century Carol
Singers

554 'The Boar's Head Carol'

Christmas

1978 (22 Nov.) One centre phosphor band (7p) or 'all-over' phosphor (others)

1071	**551**	7p multicoloured		20	20	☐	☐
1072	**552**	9p multicoloured		25	25	☐	☐
1073	**553**	11p multicoloured		30	30	☐	☐
1074	**554**	13p multicoloured		35	35	☐	☐
	Set of 4			1·00	1·00	☐	☐
	First Day Cover				1·50		☐
	Presentation Pack			1·75		☐	
	PHQ Cards (set of 4)			1·50	4·00	☐	☐
	Set of 4 Gutter Pairs			2·50			
	Set of 4 Traffic Light						
	Gutter Pairs			3·00		☐	

Collectors Pack 1978

1978 (22 Nov.) Comprises Nos 1050/7, 1059/74

Collectors Pack			7·00	☐

555 Old English Sheepdog

556 Welsh Springer Spaniel

557 West Highland Terrier

558 Irish Setter

Dogs

1979 (7 FEB.) 'All-over' phosphor

1075	**555**	9p multicoloured	20	20	☐	☐
1076	**556**	10½p multicoloured	40	30	☐	☐
1077	**557**	11p multicoloured	40	30	☐	☐
1078	**558**	13p multicoloured	40	30	☐	☐
		Set of 4	1·25	1·00	☐	☐
		First Day Cover		1·50		☐
		Presentation Pack	2·25		☐	
		PHQ Cards (set of 4)	3·00	5·00	☐	☐
		Set of 4 Gutter Pairs	2·50		☐	
		Set of 4 Traffic Light Gutter Pairs	3·75		☐	

559 Primrose

560 Daffodil

561 Bluebell

562 Snowdrop

Spring Wild Flowers

1979 (21 MAR.) 'All-over' phosphor

1079	**559**	9p multicoloured	20	20	☐	☐
1080	**560**	10½p multicoloured	40	30	☐	☐
1081	**561**	11p multicoloured	40	30	☐	☐
1082	**562**	13p multicoloured	40	30	☐	☐
		Set of 4	1·25	1·00	☐	☐
		First Day Cover		1·50		☐
		Presentation Pack	2·00		☐	
		PHQ Cards (set of 4)	2·00	4·00	☐	☐
		Set of 4 Gutter Pairs	2·50		☐	
		Set of 4 Traffic Light Gutter Pairs	3·75		☐	

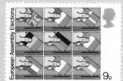

563

564

565

566

T **563/6** show hands placing the flags of the member nations into ballot boxes

First Direct Elections to European Assembly

1979 (9 MAY) Phosphorised paper

1083	**563**	9p multicoloured	20	20	☐	☐
1084	**564**	10½p multicoloured	30	30	☐	☐
1085	**565**	11p multicoloured	30	30	☐	☐
1086	**566**	13p multicoloured	30	30	☐	☐
		Set of 4	1·00	1·00	☐	☐
		First Day Cover		1·50		☐
		Presentation Pack	2·00		☐	
		PHQ Cards (set of 4)	1·50	3·50	☐	☐
		Set of 4 Gutter Pairs	2·50		☐	
		Set of 4 Traffic Light Gutter Pairs	3·75		☐	

567 Saddling 'Mahmoud' for the Derby, 1936 (Sir Alfred Munnings)

568 The Liverpool Great National Steeple Chase 1839 (aquatint by F. C. Turner)

569 The First Spring Meeting, Newmarket, 1793 (J. N. Sartorius)

570 Racing at Dorsett Ferry, Windsor, 1684 (Francis Barlow)

Horseracing Paintings and Bicentenary of The Derby (9p)

1979 (6 June) 'All-over' phosphor

1087	**567**	9p multicoloured	25	25	☐	☐
1088	**568**	10½p multicoloured	30	30	☐	☐
1089	**569**	11p multicoloured	30	30	☐	☐
1090	**570**	13p multicoloured	30	30	☐	☐
		Set of 4	1·10	1·10	☐	☐
		First Day Cover		1·75		☐
		Presentation Pack	2·00		☐	
		PHQ Cards (set of 4)	1·50	3·00	☐	☐
		Set of 4 Gutter Pairs	2·50		☐	
		Set of 4 Traffic Light Gutter Pairs	3·75		☐	

571 *The Tale of Peter Rabbit* (Beatrix Potter)

572 *The Wind in the Willows* (Kenneth Grahame)

573 *Winnie-the-Pooh* (A A Milne)

574 *Alice's Adventures in Wonderland* (Lewis Carroll)

T 571/4 depict original illustrations from the four books.

International Year of the Child

1979 (11 July) 'All-over' phosphor

1091	**571**	9p multicoloured	25	20	☐	☐
1092	**572**	10½p multicoloured	30	35	☐	☐
1093	**573**	11p multicoloured	35	40	☐	☐
1094	**574**	13p multicoloured	50	45	☐	☐
		Set of 4	1·25	1·25	☐	☐
		First Day Cover		2·25		☐
		Presentation Pack	2·25		☐	
		PHQ Cards (set of 4)	2·50	3·00	☐	☐
		Set of 4 Gutter Pairs	3·00		☐	
		Set of 4 Traffic Light Gutter Pairs	4·75		☐	

For full information on all future British issues, collectors should write to the British Post Office Philatelic Bureau, 20 Brandon Street, Edinburgh EH3 5TT

575 Sir Rowland Hill, 1795–1879

576 General Post, c 1839

577 London Post, c 1839

578 Uniform Postage, 1840

Death Centenary of Sir Rowland Hill (Postal Reformer)

1979 (22 Aug.–24 Oct.) 'All-over' phosphor

1095	**575**	10p multicoloured	25	25	☐	☐
1096	**576**	11½p multicoloured	30	35	☐	☐
1097	**577**	13p multicoloured	35	40	☐	☐
1098	**578**	15p multicoloured	50	40	☐	☐
		Set of 4	1·25	1·25	☐	☐
		First Day Cover		1·50		☐
		Presentation Pack	2·00		☐	
		PHQ Cards (set of 4)	1·50	3·00	☐	☐
		Set of 4 Gutter Pairs	2·50		☐	
		Set of 4 Traffic Light Gutter Pairs	3·75		☐	
MS1099		89×121 mm. Nos. 1095/8	1·25	1·25	☐	☐
		First Day Cover (24 Oct.)		1·75		☐

No. **MS**1099 was sold at 59½p, the premium being used for the London 1980 Stamp Exhibition.

579 Policeman on the Beat

580 Policeman directing Traffic

55

581 Mounted Policewoman

582 River Patrol Boat

150th Anniversary of Metropolitan Police

1979 (26 SEPT.) *Phosphorised paper*

1100	**579**	10p multicoloured		25	25	□	□
1101	**580**	11½p multicoloured		30	35	□	□
1102	**581**	13p multicoloured		35	40	□	□
1103	**582**	15p multicoloured		50	40	□	□
		Set of 4		1·25	1·25	□	□
		First Day Cover			1·50		□
		Presentation Pack		2·00		□	
		PHQ Cards (set of 4)		1·50	3·00	□	□
		Set of 4 Gutter Pairs		2·50		□	
		Set of 4 Traffic Light					
		Gutter Pairs		3·75		□	

583 The Three Kings

584 Angel appearing to the Shepherds

585 The Nativity

586 Mary and Joseph travelling to Bethlehem

587 The Annunciation

Christmas

1979 (21 NOV.) *One centre phosphor band (8p) or phosphorised paper (others)*

1104	**583**	8p multicoloured		20	20	□	□
1105	**584**	10p multicoloured		25	25	□	□
1106	**585**	11½p multicoloured		30	35	□	□
1107	**586**	13p multicoloured		40	40	□	□
1108	**587**	15p multicoloured		50	45	□	□
		Set of 5		1·50	1·50	□	□
		First Day Cover			1·75		□
		Presentation Pack		2·25		□	
		PHQ Cards (set of 5)		1·50	3·50	□	□
		Set of 5 Gutter Pairs		3·00		□	
		Set of 5 Traffic Light					
		Gutter Pairs		3·75		□	

Collectors Pack 1979

1979 (21 NOV.) *Comprises Nos.* 1075/98. 1100/8

	Collectors Pack		8·50	□

588 Kingfisher

589 Dipper

590 Moorhen

591 Yellow Wagtails

Centenary of Wild Bird Protection Act

1980 (16 JAN.) *Phosphorised paper*

1109	**588**	10p multicoloured		25	25	□	□
1110	**589**	11½p multicoloured		40	35	□	□
1111	**590**	13p multicoloured		50	40	□	□
1112	**591**	15p multicoloured		55	45	□	□
		Set of 4		1·50	1·25	□	□
		First Day Cover			1·75		□
		Presentation Pack		2·00		□	
		PHQ Cards (set of 4)		1·50	3·00	□	□
		Set of 4 Gutter Pairs		3·00		□	

592 *Rocket* approaching Moorish Arch, Liverpool

593 First and Second Class Carriages passing through Olive Mount Cutting

594 Third Class Carriage and Cattle Truck crossing Chat Moss

595 Horsebox and Carriage Truck near Bridgewater Canal

596 Goods Truck and Mail-coach at Manchester

T 592/6 were printed together, *se-tenant* in horizontal strips of 5 throughout the sheet.

150th Anniversary of Liverpool and Manchester Railway

1980 (12 Mar.) *Phosphorised paper*

1113	**592**	12p multicoloured	25	25	☐	☐
		a. Strip of 5.				
		Nos. 1113/17	1·50	1·60	☐	☐
1114	**593**	12p multicoloured	25	25	☐	☐
1115	**594**	12p multicoloured	25	25	☐	☐
1116	**595**	12p multicoloured	25	25	☐	☐
1117	**596**	12p multicoloured	25	25	☐	☐
		Set of 5	1·50	1·10	☐	☐
		First Day Cover		1·50	☐	
		Presentation Pack	2·75		☐	
		PHQ Cards (set of 5)	1·50	3·75	☐	☐
		Gutter block of 10	3·25		☐	

Minimum Price. The minimum price quoted is 10p. This represents a handling charge rather than a basis for valuing common stamps. Where the actual value of a stamp is less than 10p this may be apparent when set prices are shown, particularly for sets including a number of 10p stamps. It therefore follows that in valuing common stamps the 10p catalogue price should not be reckoned automatically since it covers a variation in real scarcity.

597 Montage of London Buildings

"London 1980" International Stamp Exhibition

1980 (9 Apr–7 May) *Phosphorised paper. Perf* $14\frac{1}{2} \times 14$

1118	**597**	50p agate	1·50	1·25	☐	☐
		First Day Cover		1·50		☐
		Presentation Pack	2·00			☐
		PHQ Card	50	1·75		☐
		Gutter Pair	3·00			☐
MS1119		90×123 mm. No. 1118	1·50	1·50	☐	☐
		First Day Cover (7 May)		1·75		☐

No. **MS**1119 was sold at 75p, the premium being used for the exhibition.

598 Buckingham Palace

599 The Albert Memorial

600 Royal Opera House

601 Hampton Court

17½p Kensington Palace

602 Kensington Palace

London Landmarks
1980 (7 MAY) *Phosphorised paper*

1120	**598**	10½p multicoloured	25	25	□	□
1121	**599**	12p multicoloured	30	30	□	□
1122	**600**	13½p multicoloured	35	35	□	□
1123	**601**	15p multicoloured	40	40	□	□
1124	**602**	17½p multicoloured	40	40	□	□
		Set of 5	1·50	1·50	□	□
		First Day Cover		1·75		□
		Presentation Pack	2·50		□	
		PHQ Cards (set of 5)	1·50	3·00	□	□
		Set of 5 Gutter Pairs	3·00		□	

12p

603 Charlotte Bronte
(*Jane Eyre*)

13½p

604 George Eliot (*The Mill on the Floss*)

15p

605 Emily Bronte
(*Wuthering Heights*)

17½p

606 Mrs Gaskell (*North and South*)

T 603/6 show authoresses and scenes from their novels. T 603/4 also include the "Europa" C.E.P.T. emblem

Famous Authoresses
1980 (9 JULY) *Phosphorised paper*

1125	**603**	12p multicoloured	30	30	□	□
1126	**604**	13½p multicoloured	35	35	□	□
1127	**605**	15p multicoloured	40	45	□	□
1128	**606**	17½p multicoloured	60	60	□	□
		Set of 4	1·50	1·50	□	□
		First Day Cover		1·50		□
		Presentation Pack	2·50		□	
		PHQ Cards (set of 4)	1·50	3·00	□	□
		Set of 4 Gutter Pairs	3·00		□	

HER MAJESTY QUEEN ELIZABETH THE QUEEN MOTHER
80TH BIRTHDAY
12p

607 Queen Elizabeth the Queen Mother

80th Birthday of Queen Elizabeth the Queen Mother
1980 (4 AUG.) *Phosphorised paper*

1129	**607**	12p multicoloured	75	75	□	□
		First Day Cover		1·00		□
		PHQ Card	50	1·25	□	□
		Gutter Pair	1·50		□	

12p Sir Henry Wood

608 Sir Henry Wood

13½p Sir Thomas Beecham

609 Sir Thomas Beecham

15p Sir Malcolm Sargent

610 Sir Malcolm Sargent

17½p Sir John Barbirolli

611 Sir John Barbirolli

British Conductors
1980 (10 SEPT.) *Phosphorised paper*

1130	**608**	12p multicoloured	30	30	□	□
1131	**609**	13½p multicoloured	35	40	□	□
1132	**610**	15p multicoloured	45	45	□	□
1133	**611**	17½p multicoloured	55	50	□	□
		Set of 4	1·50	1·50	□	□
		First Day Cover		1·50		□
		Presentation Pack	2·00		□	
		PHQ Cards (set of 4)	1·50	2·50	□	□
		Set of 4 Gutter Pairs	3·00		□	

612 Running

613 Rugby

614 Boxing

615 Cricket

618 Apples and Mistletoe

619 Crown, Chains and Bell

620 Holly

Sports Centenaries

1980 (10 Oct.) *Phosphorised paper. Perf* 14 × 14½

1134	**612**	12p multicoloured	30	30	☐	☐
1135	**613**	13½p multicoloured	35	40	☐	☐
1136	**614**	15p multicoloured	40	40	☐	☐
1137	**615**	17½p multicoloured	60	55	☐	☐
		Set of 4	1·50	1·50	☐	☐
		First Day Cover		1·50		☐
		Presentation Pack	2·00		☐	
		PHQ Cards (set of 4)	1·50	2·50	☐	☐
		Set of 4 Gutter Pairs	3·00		☐	

Centenaries:— 12p Amateur Athletics Association; 13½p Welsh Rugby Union; 15p Amateur Boxing Association; 17½p First England v Australia Test Match

Christmas

1980 (19 Nov.) *One centre phosphor band (10p) or phosphorised paper (others)*

1138	**616**	10p multicoloured	25	25	☐	☐
1139	**617**	12p multicoloured	30	35	☐	☐
1140	**618**	13½p multicoloured	35	40	☐	☐
1141	**619**	15p multicoloured	40	40	☐	☐
1142	**620**	17½p multicoloured	50	40	☐	☐
		Set of 5	1·60	1·60	☐	☐
		First Day Cover		1·60		☐
		Presentation Pack	2·25		☐	
		PHQ Cards (set of 5)	1·50	2·50	☐	☐
		Set of 5 Gutter Pairs	3·25		☐	

Collectors Pack 1980

1980 (19 Nov.) *Comprises Nos.* 1109/18, 1120/42

	Collectors Pack		10·00	☐

616 Christmas Tree

617 Candles

621 St. Valentine's Day

622 Morris Dancers

623 Lammastide

624 Medieval Mummers

T **621**/**22** also include the "Europa" C.E.P.T. emblem.

Folklore

1981 (6 FEB.) *Phosphorised paper*

1143	**621**	14p multicoloured	35	35	☐ ☐
1144	**622**	18p multicoloured	45	50	☐ ☐
1145	**623**	22p multicoloured	60	60	☐ ☐
1146	**624**	25p multicoloured	75	70	☐ ☐
		Set of 4	2·00	2·00	☐ ☐
		First Day Cover		2·00	☐
		Presentation Pack	2·50		☐
		PHQ Cards (set of 4)	1·50	2·50	☐ ☐
		Set of 4 Gutter Pairs	4·00		☐

625 Blind Man with Guide Dog

626 Hands spelling "Deaf" in Sign Language

627 Disabled Man in Wheelchair

628 Disabled Artist painting with Foot

International Year of the Disabled

1981 (25 MAR.) *Phosphorised paper*

1147	**625**	14p multicoloured	35	35	☐ ☐
1148	**626**	18p multicoloured	45	50	☐ ☐
1149	**627**	22p multicoloured	60	60	☐ ☐
1150	**628**	25p multicoloured	75	70	☐ ☐
		Set of 4	2·00	2·00	☐ ☐
		First Day Cover		2·00	☐
		Presentation Pack	2·50		☐
		PHQ Cards (set of 4)	1·50	2·75	☐ ☐
		Set of 4 Gutter Pairs	4·00		☐

629 *Aglais urticae*

630 *Maculinea arion*

631 *Inachis io*

632 *Carterocephalus palaemon*

Butterflies

1981 (13 MAY) *Phosphorised paper*

1151	**629**	14p multicoloured	35	35	☐ ☐
1152	**630**	18p multicoloured	60	50	☐ ☐
1153	**631**	22p multicoloured	70	65	☐ ☐
1154	**632**	25p multicoloured	80	75	☐ ☐
		Set of 4	2·25	2·00	☐ ☐
		First Day Cover		2·25	☐
		Presentation Pack	2·50		☐
		PHQ Cards (set of 4)	2·00	3·00	☐ ☐
		Set of 4 Gutter Pairs	4·50		☐

633 Glenfinnan, Scotland

634 Derwentwater, England

635 Stackpole Head, Wales

636 Giant's Causeway, N. Ireland

637 St Kilda, Scotland

50th Anniversary of National Trust for Scotland

1981 (24 June) *Phosphorised paper*

1155	**633**	14p multicoloured	30	30	☐	☐
1156	**634**	18p multicoloured	40	40	☐	☐
1157	**635**	20p multicoloured	50	50	☐	☐
1158	**636**	22p multicoloured	60	60	☐	☐
1159	**637**	25p multicoloured	70	70	☐	☐
		Set of 5	2·25	2·25	☐	☐
		First Day Cover		2·25		☐
		Presentation Pack	2·75		☐	
		PHQ Cards (set of 5)	2·00	2·75	☐	☐
		Set of 5 Gutter Pairs	4·50		☐	

638 Prince Charles and Lady Diana Spencer

Royal Wedding

1981 (22 July) *Phosphorised paper*

1160	**638**	14p multicoloured	3·50	3·00	☐	☐
1161		25p multicoloured	4·50	5·00	☐	☐
		Set of 2	8·00	8·00	☐	☐
		First Day Cover		8·00		☐
		Presentation Pack	9·00		☐	
		Souvenir Book	10·00		☐	
		PHQ Cards (set of 2)	3·00	8·50	☐	☐
		Set of 2 Gutter Pairs	16·00		☐	

639 "Expeditions"

640 "Skills"

641 "Service"

642 "Recreation"

25th Anniversary of Duke of Edinburgh Award Scheme

1981 (12 Aug.) *Phosphorised paper. Perf 14*

1162	**639**	14p multicoloured	35	35	☐	☐
1163	**640**	18p multicoloured	50	50	☐	☐
1164	**641**	22p multicoloured	60	60	☐	☐
1165	**642**	25p multicoloured	70	70	☐	☐
		Set of 4	2·00	2·00	☐	☐
		First Day Cover		2·00		☐
		Presentation Pack	2·50		☐	
		PHQ Cards (set of 4)	1·60	2·25	☐	☐
		Set of 4 Gutter Pairs	4·00		☐	

643 Cockle-Dredging from *Linsey II*

644 Hauling Trawl Net

645 Lobster Potting

646 Hoisting Seine Net

Fishing Industry

1981 (23 Sept.) *Phosphorised paper*

1166	**643**	14p multicoloured	35	35	☐	☐
1167	**644**	18p multicoloured	50	50	☐	☐
1168	**645**	22p multicoloured	60	60	☐	☐
1169	**646**	25p multicoloured	70	65	☐	☐
		Set of 4	2·00	2·00	☐	☐
		First Day Cover		2·00		☐
		Presentation Pack	2·50		☐	
		PHQ Cards (set of 4)	2·00	2·50	☐	☐
		Set of 4 Gutter Pairs	4·00		☐	

Nos. 1166/9 were issued on the occasion of the centenary of Royal National Mission to Deep Sea Fishermen.

647 Father Christmas

648 Jesus Christ

652 Charles Darwin and Giant Tortoises

653 Darwin and Marine Iguanas

649 Flying Angel

650 Joseph and Mary arriving at Bethlehem

654 Darwin. Cactus Ground Finch and Large Ground Finch

655 Darwin and Prehistoric Skulls

Death Centenary of Charles Darwin

1982 (10 FEB.) *Phosphorised paper*

1175	**652**	15½p multicoloured ..	35	35	☐	☐
1176	**653**	19½p multicoloured ..	60	60	☐	☐
1177	**654**	26p multicoloured ..	70	70	☐	☐
1178	**655**	29p multicoloured ..	75	75	☐	☐
		Set of 4	2·25	2·25	☐	☐
		First Day Cover		2·25		☐
		Presentation Pack	3·00		☐	
		PHQ Cards (set of 4) ..	2·50	6·50	☐	☐
		Set of 4 Gutter Pairs ..	4·50		☐	

651 Three Kings approaching Bethlehem

Christmas. Children's Pictures

1981 (18 NOV.) *One phosphor band (11½p) or phosphorised paper (others)*

1170	**647**	11½p multicoloured ..	30	30	☐	☐
1171	**648**	14p multicoloured ..	40	40	☐	☐
1172	**649**	18p multicoloured ..	50	50	☐	☐
1173	**650**	22p multicoloured ..	60	60	☐	☐
1174	**651**	25p multicoloured ..	70	70	☐	☐
		Set of 5	2·25	2·25	☐	☐
		First Day Cover		2·25		☐
		Presentation Pack	3·00		☐	
		PHQ Cards (set of 5) ..	2·00	3·50	☐	☐
		Set of 5 Gutter Pairs	4·50		☐	

Collectors Pack 1981

1981 (18 NOV.) *Comprises Nos. 1143/74*

	Collectors Pack	20·00	☐

656 Boys' Brigade

657 Girls' Brigade

658 Boy Scout Movement

659 Girl Guide Movement

For full information on all future British issues, collectors should write to the British Post Office Philatelic Bureau, 20 Brandon Street, Edinburgh EH3 5TT.

1982 (24 MAR.) *Phosphorised paper*

1179	**656**	15½p multicoloured	35	35	☐	☐
1180	**657**	19½p multicoloured	60	50	☐	☐
1181	**658**	26p multicoloured	85	75	☐	☐
1182	**659**	29p multicoloured	1·00	90	☐	☐
		Set of 4	2·50	2·25	☐	☐
		First Day Cover		2·25		☐
		Presentation Pack	3·50		☐	
		PHQ Cards (set of 4)	2·50	6·50	☐	
		Set of 4 Gutter Pairs	5·00		☐	

Nos. 1179/82 were issued on the occasion of the 75th anniversary of the Boy Scout Movement, the 125th birth anniversary of Lord Baden-Powell and the centenary of the Boys' Brigade (1983).

660 Ballerina

661 Harlequin

662 Hamlet

663 Opera Singer

Europa. British Theatre

1982 (28 APR.) *Phosphorised paper*

1183	**660**	15½p multicoloured	35	35	☐	☐
1184	**661**	19½p multicoloured	60	50	☐	☐
1185	**662**	26p multicoloured	90	75	☐	☐
1186	**663**	29p multicoloured	1·25	90	☐	☐
		Set of 4	2·75	2·25	☐	☐
		First Day Cover		2·25		☐
		Presentation Pack	3·25		☐	
		PHQ Cards (set of 4)	2·50	6·50	☐	
		Set of 4 Gutter Pairs	5·50		☐	

664 Henry VIII and *Mary Rose*

665 Admiral Blake and *Triumph*

666 Lord Nelson and HMS *Victory*

667 Lord Fisher and HMS *Dreadnought*

668 Viscount Cunningham and HMS *Warspite*

Maritime Heritage

1982 (16 JUNE) *Phosphorised paper*

1187	**664**	15½p multicoloured	35	35	☐	☐
1188	**665**	19½p multicoloured	60	60	☐	☐
1189	**666**	24p multicoloured	70	70	☐	☐
1190	**667**	26p multicoloured	80	80	☐	☐
1191	**668**	29p multicoloured	90	90	☐	☐
		Set of 5	3·00	3·00	☐	☐
		First Day Cover		3·00		☐
		Presentation Pack	3·75		☐	
		PHQ Cards (set of 5)	3·00	6·50	☐	
		Set of 5 Gutter Pairs	6·00		☐	

669 "Strawberry Thief" (William Morris)

670 Untitled (Steiner and Co)

671 "Cherry Orchard"
(Paul Nash)

672 "Chevron" (Andrew
Foster)

British Textiles

1982 (23 JULY) *Phosphorised paper*

1192	**669**	15½p multicoloured	35	35	☐	☐
1193	**670**	19½p multicoloured	55	55	☐	☐
1194	**671**	26p multicoloured	70	70	☐	☐
1195	**672**	29p multicoloured	90	90	☐	☐
		Set of 4	2·25	2·25	☐	☐
		First Day Cover		2·50	☐	
		Presentation Pack	3·25		☐	
		PHQ Cards (set of 4)	3·00	6·50	☐	☐
		Set of 4 Gutter Pairs	4·50		☐	

Nos 1192/5 were issued on the occasion of the 250th birth anniversary of Sir Richard Arkwright (inventor of spinning machine).

673 Development of Communications

674 Modern Technological Aids

Information Technology

1982 (8 SEPT.) *Phosphorised paper. Perf 14 × 15*

1196	**673**	15½p multicoloured	45	50	☐	☐
1197	**674**	26p multicoloured	80	85	☐	☐
		Set of 2	1·25	1·25	☐	☐
		First Day Cover		1·50	☐	
		Presentation Pack	2·00		☐	
		PHQ Cards (set of 2)	1·50	4·50	☐	☐
		Set of 2 Gutter Pairs	2·50		☐	

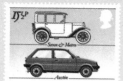

675 Austin "Seven" and "Metro"   **676** Ford "Model T" and "Escort"

677 Jaguar "SS1" and "XJ6"   **678** Rolls-Royce "Silver Ghost" and "Silver Spirit"

British Motor Industry

1982 (13 OCT.) *Phosphorised paper. Perf 14½ × 14*

1198	**675**	15½p multicoloured	50	50	☐	☐
1199	**676**	19½p multicoloured	70	70	☐	☐
1200	**677**	26p multicoloured	90	90	☐	☐
1201	**678**	29p multicoloured	1·25	1·25	☐	☐
		Set of 4	3·00	3·00	☐	☐
		First Day Cover		3·00	☐	
		Presentation Pack	3·75		☐	
		PHQ Cards (set of 4)	3·00	7·00	☐	☐
		Set of 4 Gutter Pairs	6·00		☐	

679 "While Shepherds Watched"   **680** "The Holly and the Ivy"

681 "I Saw Three Ships"   **682** "We Three Kings"

683 "Good King Wenceslas"

Christmas. Carols

1982 (17 Nov) One phosphor band (12½p) or phosphorised paper (others)

1202	**679**	12½p multicoloured		30	30	☐	☐
1203	**680**	15½p multicoloured		40	40	☐	☐
1204	**681**	19½p multicoloured		70	70	☐	☐
1205	**682**	26p multicoloured		80	80	☐	☐
1206	**683**	29p multicoloured		90	90	☐	☐
		Set of 5		2·75	2·75	☐	☐
		First Day Cover			2·75	☐	
		Presentation Pack		3·25		☐	
		PHQ Cards (set of 5)		3·00	7·00	☐	☐
		Set of 5 Gutter Pairs		5·50		☐	

Collectors Pack 1982

1982 (17 Nov) Comprises Nos. 1175/1206

Collectors Pack		21·00	☐

684 Salmon **685** Pike

686 Trout **687** Perch

British River Fishes

1983 (26 Jan.) Phosphorised paper

1207	**684**	15½p multicoloured		35	35	☐	☐
1208	**685**	19½p multicoloured		65	55	☐	☐
1209	**686**	26p multicoloured		80	70	☐	☐
1210	**687**	29p multicoloured		1·00	90	☐	☐
		Set of 4		2·50	2·25	☐	☐
		First Day Cover			2·50	☐	
		Presentation Pack		3·00		☐	
		PHQ Cards (set of 4)		3·00	6·50	☐	☐
		Set of 4 Gutter Pairs		5·00		☐	

688 Tropical Island **689** Desert

690 Temperate Farmland **691** Mountain Range

Commonwealth Day. Geographical Regions

1983 (9 Mar.) Phosphorised paper

1211	**688**	15½p multicoloured		35	35	☐	☐
1212	**689**	19½p multicoloured		55	55	☐	☐
1213	**690**	26p multicoloured		70	70	☐	☐
1214	**691**	29p multicoloured		90	90	☐	☐
		Set of 4		2·25	2·25	☐	☐
		First Day Cover			2·50	☐	
		Presentation Pack		3·25		☐	
		PHQ Cards (set of 4)		3·00	6·50	☐	☐
		Set of 4 Gutter Pairs		4·50		☐	

692 Humber Bridge **693** Thames Flood Barrier

694 Iolair (oilfield emergency support vessel)

Europa. Engineering Achievements

1983 (25 May) *Phosphorised paper*

1215	**692**	16p multicoloured		45	45	☐	☐
1216	**693**	20½p multicoloured		95	1·10	☐	☐
1217	**694**	28p multicoloured		1·10	1·25	☐	☐
		Set of 3		2·25	2·50	☐	☐
		First Day Cover			2·50		☐
		Presentation Pack		3·50		☐	
		PHQ Cards (set of 3)		2·50	6·00	☐	☐
		Set of 3 Gutter Pairs		4·50		☐	

British Army Uniforms

1983 (6 July) *Phosphorised paper*

1218	**695**	16p multicoloured		40	40	☐	☐
1219	**696**	20½p multicoloured		70	70	☐	☐
1220	**697**	26p multicoloured		85	85	☐	☐
1221	**698**	28p multicoloured		85	85	☐	☐
1222	**699**	31p multicoloured		1·10	1·10	☐	☐
		Set of 5		3·50	3·50	☐	☐
		First Day Cover			3·25		☐
		Presentation Pack		4·50		☐	
		PHQ Cards (set of 5)		3·00	6·00	☐	☐
		Set of 5 Gutter Pairs		7·00		☐	

Nos. 1218/22 were issued on the occasion of the 350th anniversary of The Royal Scots, the senior line regiment of the British Army.

695 Musketeer and Pikeman. The Royal Scots (1633)

696 Fusilier and Ensign. The Royal Welch Fusiliers (mid-18th century)

20TH CENTURY GARDEN **SISSINGHURST**

700 20th-Century Garden. Sissinghurst

19TH CENTURY GARDEN **BIDDULPH GRANGE**

701 19th-Century Garden. Biddulph Grange

697 Riflemen. 95th Rifles (The Royal Green Jackets) (1805)

698 Sergeant (khaki service uniform) and Guardsman (full dress). The Irish Guards (1900)

18TH CENTURY GARDEN **BLENHEIM**

702 18th-Century Garden. Blenheim

17TH CENTURY GARDEN **PITMEDDEN**

703 17th-Century Garden. Pitmedden

British Gardens

1983 (24 Aug.) *Phosphorised paper. Perf 14*

1223	**700**	16p multicoloured		40	40	☐	☐
1224	**701**	20½p multicoloured		50	50	☐	☐
1225	**702**	28p multicoloured		90	90	☐	☐
1226	**703**	31p multicoloured		1·00	1·00	☐	☐
		Set of 4		2·50	2·50	☐	☐
		First Day Cover			2·75		☐
		Presentation Pack		3·50		☐	
		PHQ Cards (set of 4)		3·00	6·00	☐	☐
		Set of 4 Gutter Pairs		5·00		☐	

699 Paratroopers. The Parachute Regiment (1983)

704 Merry-go-round

705 Big Wheel, Helter-skelter and Performing Animals

706 Side-shows

707 Early Produce Fair

British Fairs

1983 (5 Oct) *Phosphorised paper.*

1227	704	16p multicoloured	40	40	☐	☐
1228	705	20½p multicoloured	65	65	☐	☐
1229	706	28p multicoloured	85	85	☐	☐
1230	707	31p multicoloured	90	90	☐	☐
		Set of 4	2·50	2·50	☐	☐
		First Day Cover		2·75		☐
		Presentation Pack	3·50		☐	
		PHQ Cards (set of 4)	3·00	6·00	☐	☐
		Set of 4 Gutter Pairs	5·00		☐	

Nos. 1227/30 were issued to mark the 850th Anniversary of St. Bartholomew's Fair, Smithfield, London.

708 "Christmas Post" (pillar-box)

709 "The Three Kings" (chimney-pots)

710 "World at Peace" (Dove and Blackbird)

711 "Light of Christmas" (street lamp)

712 "Christmas Dove" (hedge sculpture)

Christmas

1983 (16 Nov) *One phosphor band (12½p) or phosphorised paper (others)*

1231	708	12½p multicoloured	30	30	☐	☐
1232	709	16p multicoloured	35	35	☐	☐
1233	710	20½p multicoloured	60	60	☐	☐
1234	711	28p multicoloured	70	80	☐	☐
1235	712	31p multicoloured	85	1·00	☐	☐
		Set of 5	2·50	2·75	☐	☐
		First Day Cover		2·75		☐
		Presentation Pack	3·50		☐	
		PHQ Cards (set of 5)	3·00	6·00	☐	☐
		Set of 5 Gutter Pairs	5·00		☐	

Collectors Pack 1983

1983 (16 Nov) *Comprises Nos. 1207/35*

	Collectors Pack	35·00	☐

713 Arms of the College of Arms

714 Arms of King Richard III (founder)

715 Arms of the Earl Marshal of England

716 Arms of the City of London

500th Anniversary of College of Arms

1984 (17 Jan.) *Phosphorised paper. Perf 14½*

1236	713	16p multicoloured		40	40	☐ ☐
1237	714	20½p multicoloured		60	60	☐ ☐
1238	715	28p multicoloured		85	85	☐ ☐
1239	716	31p multicoloured		95	95	☐ ☐
		Set of 4		2·50	2·50	☐ ☐
		First Day Cover			2·50	☐
		Presentation Pack		3·50		☐
		PHQ Cards (set of 4)		3·00	6·00	☐ ☐
		Set of 4 Gutter Pairs		5·00		

717 Highland Cow

718 Chillingham Wild Bull

719 Hereford Bull

720 Welsh Black Bull

721 Irish Moiled Cow

British Cattle

1984 (6 Mar.) *Phosphorised paper.*

1240	717	16p multicoloured		40	40	☐ ☐
1241	718	20½p multicoloured		65	65	☐ ☐
1242	719	26p multicoloured		70	70	☐ ☐
1243	720	28p multicoloured		70	70	☐ ☐
1244	721	31p multicoloured		90	90	☐ ☐
		Set of 5		3·00	3·00	☐ ☐
		First Day Cover			3·00	☐
		Presentation Pack		4·25		☐
		PHQ Cards (set of 5)		3·00	6·00	☐ ☐
		Set of 5 Gutter Pairs		6·00		

Nos. 1240/4 marked the centenary of the Highland Cattle Society and the bicentenary of the Royal Highland and Agricultural Society of Scotland.

722 Festival Hall, Liverpool

723 Milburngate Shopping Centre, Durham

724 Bush House, Bristol

725 Commercial Street Housing Scheme, Perth

Urban Renewal

1984 (10 Apr.) *Phosphorised paper.*

1245	722	16p multicoloured		40	40	☐ ☐
1246	723	20½p multicoloured		60	60	☐ ☐
1247	724	28p multicoloured		90	90	☐ ☐
1248	725	31p multicoloured		90	90	☐ ☐
		Set of 4		2·50	2·50	☐ ☐
		First Day Cover			3·00	☐
		Presentation Pack		3·50		☐
		PHQ Cards (set of 4)		3·00	6·00	☐ ☐
		Set of 4 Gutter Pairs		5·00		☐

Nos. 1245/8 mark the opening of the International Gardens Festival, Liverpool, and the 150th anniversaries of the Royal Institute of British Architects and the Chartered Institute of Building.

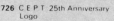

726 C.E.P.T. 25th Anniversary Logo

727 Abduction of Europa

Nos. 1249/50 and 1251/2 were each printed together, *se-tenant*, in horizontal pairs throughout the sheets.

Europa. 25th Anniversary of C.E.P.T. and 2nd European Parliamentary Elections

1984 (15 MAY) *Phosphorised paper*.

1249	**726**	16p greenish slate. dp blue and gold	90	90	☐	☐	
	a.	Horiz pair. Nos. 1249/50	1·75	1·75	☐	☐	
1250	**727**	16p greenish slate. dp bl, blk and gold	90	90	☐	☐	
1251	**726**	20½p Venetian red, deep magenta and gold	1·60	1·60	☐	☐	
	a.	Horizontal pair Nos. 1251/2	3·25	3·25	☐	☐	
1252	**727**	20½p Venetian red, deep magenta, black and gold	1·60	1·60	☐	☐	
		Set of 4	4·50	4·50	☐	☐	
		First Day Cover		4·50	☐		
		Presentation Pack	5·00		☐		
		PHQ Cards (set of 4)	3·00	6·00	☐	☐	
		Set of 2 Gutter Blocks of 4	9·00		☐		

728 Lancaster House

London Economic Summit Conference

1984 (5 JUNE) *Phosphorised paper*.

1253	**728**	31p multicoloured	1·00	1·00	☐	☐
		First Day Cover		2·00		☐
		PHQ Card	1·00	2·75	☐	☐
		Gutter Pair	2·00		☐	

729 View of Earth from "Apollo 11"

730 Navigational Chart of English Channel

731 Greenwich Observatory

732 Sir George Airey's Transit Telescope

Centenary of Greenwich Meridian

1984 (26 JUNE) *Phosphorised paper. Perf 14 × 14½*

1254	**729**	16p multicoloured	40	40	☐	☐
1255	**730**	20½p multicoloured	65	65	☐	☐
1256	**731**	28p multicoloured	85	90	☐	☐
1257	**732**	31p multicoloured	90	1·10	☐	☐
		Set of 4	2·50	2·75	☐	☐
		First Day Cover		2·75		☐
		Presentation Pack	3·75		☐	
		PHQ Cards (set of 4)	3·00	6·00	☐	☐
		Set of 4 Gutter Pairs	5·00		☐	

733 Bath Mail Coach, 1784

734 Attack on Exeter Mail, 1816

735 Norwich Mail in Thunderstorm, 1827

736 Holyhead and Liverpool Mails leaving London, 1828

737 Edinburgh Mail Snowbound, 1831

T 733/7 were printed together, *se-tenant* in horizontal strips of 5 throughout the sheet.

Bicentenary of First Mail Coach Run, Bath and Bristol to London

1984 (31 JULY) *Phosphorised paper*

1258	**733**	16p multicoloured	60	40	☐	☐
		a. Horiz strip of 5.				
		Nos. 1258/62	2·75	2·75	☐	☐
1259	**734**	16p multicoloured	60	40	☐	☐
1260	**735**	16p multicoloured	60	40	☐	☐
1261	**736**	16p multicoloured	60	40	☐	☐
1262	**737**	16p multicoloured	60	40	☐	☐
		Set of 5	2·75	1·75	☐	☐
		First Day Cover		2·75		☐
		Presentation Pack	3·75		☐	
		Souvenir Book	6·00		☐	
		PHQ Cards (set of 5)	3·00	6·50	☐	☐
		Gutter Block of 10	5·50		☐	

738 Nigerian Clinic

739 Violinist and Acropolis, Athens

740 Building Project, Sri Lanka

741 British Council Library

50th Anniversary of The British Council

1984 (25 SEPT.) *Phosphorised paper*

1263	**738**	17p multicoloured	50	50	☐	☐
1264	**739**	22p multicoloured	65	65	☐	☐
1265	**740**	31p multicoloured	90	90	☐	☐
1266	**741**	34p multicoloured	1·00	1·00	☐	☐
		Set of 4	2·75	2·75	☐	☐
		First Day Cover		2·75		☐
		Presentation Pack	3·50		☐	
		PHQ Cards (set of 4)	3·00	6·00	☐	☐
		Set of 4 Gutter Pairs	5·50		☐	

For full information on all future British issues, collectors should write to the British Post Office Philatelic Bureau, 20 Brandon Street, Edinburgh EH3 5TT.

742 The Holy Family

743 Arrival in Bethlehem

744 Shepherd and Lamb

745 Virgin and Child

746 Offering of Frankincense

Christmas

1984 (20 Nov.) *One phosphor band (13p) or phosphorised paper (others)*

1267	**742**	13p multicoloured	30	30	☐	☐
1268	**743**	17p multicoloured	50	50	☐	☐
1269	**744**	22p multicoloured	60	60	☐	☐
1270	**745**	31p multicoloured	95	95	☐	☐
1271	**746**	34p multicoloured	1·00	1·00	☐	☐
		Set of 5	3·00	3·00	☐	☐
		First Day Cover		3·00		☐
		Presentation Pack	3·75		☐	
		PHQ Cards (set of 5)	3·00	6·00	☐	☐
		Set of 5 Gutter Pairs	6·00		☐	

Collectors Pack 1984

1984 (20 Nov.) *Comprises Nos.* 1236/71

	Collectors Pack	35·00	☐

Post Office Yearbook

1984. *Comprises Nos.* 1236/71 *in hardbound book with slip case.*

	Yearbook	75·00	☐

747 "The Flying Scotsman"

748 "The Golden Arrow"

749 "The Cheltenham Flyer"

750 "The Royal Scot"

751 "The Cornish Riviera"

754 *Decticus verrucivorus* (bush-cricket)

755 *Lucanus cervus* (stag beetle)

756 *Anax imperator* (dragonfly)

Famous Trains

1985 (22 Jan.) *Phosphorised paper*

1272	**747**	17p multicoloured	..	50	50	☐	☐
1273	**748**	22p multicoloured	..	85	70	☐	☐
1274	**749**	29p multicoloured	..	1·00	90	☐	☐
1275	**750**	31p multicoloured	..	1·25	1·00	☐	☐
1276	**751**	34p multicoloured	..	1·40	1·10	☐	☐
		Set of 5	..	4·50	4·00	☐	☐
		First Day Cover	..		5·00		☐
		Presentation Pack	..	5·25		☐	
		PHQ Cards (set of 5)	..	4·00	11·00	☐	☐
		Set of 5 Gutter Pairs	..	9·00		☐	

Nos. 1272/6 were issued on the occasion of the 150th anniversary of the Great Western Railway Company.

Insects

1985 (12 March) *Phosphorised paper*

1277	**752**	17p multicoloured	..	40	40	☐	☐
1278	**753**	22p multicoloured	..	60	60	☐	☐
1279	**754**	29p multicoloured	..	80	80	☐	☐
1280	**755**	31p multicoloured	..	90	90	☐	☐
1281	**756**	34p multicoloured	..	90	90	☐	☐
		Set of 5	..	3·25	3·25	☐	☐
		First Day Cover	..		3·50		☐
		Presentation Pack	..	4·00		☐	
		PHQ Cards (set of 5)	..	3·00	6·50	☐	☐
		Set of 5 Gutter Pairs	..	6·50		☐	

Nos. 1277/81 were issued on the occasion of the centenaries of the Royal Entomological Society of London's Royal Charter and of the Selborne Society.

752 *Bombus terrestris* (bee)

753 *Coccinella septempunctata* (ladybird)

757 "Water Music", by Handel

758 "The Planets", by Holst

THIRTY·ONE·PENCE

THE·FIRST·CUCKOO
Frederick Delius

759 "The First Cuckoo", by Delius

THIRTY·FOUR·PENCE

SEA·PICTURES
Edward Elgar

760 "Sea Pictures", by Elgar

Europa – European Music Year

1985 (14 MAY) *Phosphorised paper. Perf* 14½

1282	**757**	17p multicoloured	65	65	☐	☐
1283	**758**	22p multicoloured	90	90	☐	☐
1284	**759**	31p multicoloured	1·40	1·40	☐	☐
1285	**760**	34p multicoloured	1·50	1·50	☐	☐
		Set of 4	4·00	4·00	☐	☐
		First Day Cover		4·00	☐	
		Presentation Pack	4·50		☐	
		PHQ Cards (set of 4)	3·00	6·00	☐	☐
		Set of 4 Gutter Pairs	8·00		☐	

Nos. 1282/5 were issued on the occasion of the 300th birth anniversary of Handel.

761 R.N.L.I. Lifeboat and Signal Flags

762 Beachy Head Lighthouse and Chart

763 "Marecs A" Communications Satellite and Dish Aerials

764 Buoys

Safety at Sea

1985 (18 JUNE) *Phosphorised paper. Perf* 14

1286	**761**	17p multicoloured	50	50	☐	☐
1287	**762**	22p multicoloured	65	65	☐	☐
1288	**763**	31p multicoloured	1·10	1·10	☐	☐
1289	**764**	34p multicoloured	1·10	1·10	☐	☐
		Set of 4	3·00	3·00	☐	☐
		First Day Cover		3·50	☐	
		Presentation Pack	4·25		☐	
		PHQ Cards (set of 4)	3·00	6·00	☐	☐
		Set of 4 Gutter Pairs	6·00		☐	

Nos. 1286/9 were issued on the occasion of the bicentenary of the unimmersible lifeboat and the 50th anniversary of Radar.

765 Datapost Motorcyclist, City of London

766 Rural Postbus

767 Parcel Delivery in Winter

768 Town Letter Delivery

350 Years of Royal Mail Public Postal Service

1985 (30 JULY) *Phosphorised paper*

1290	**765**	17p multicoloured	50	50	☐	☐
1291	**766**	22p multicoloured	65	65	☐	☐
1292	**767**	31p multicoloured	1·10	1·10	☐	☐
1293	**768**	34p multicoloured	1·10	1·10	☐	☐
		Set of 4	3·00	3·00	☐	☐
		First Day Cover		3·25	☐	
		Presentation Pack	4·25		☐	
		PHQ Cards (set of 4)	3·00	6·00	☐	☐
		Set of 4 Gutter Pairs	6·00		☐	

769 King Arthur and Merlin

770 The Lady of the Lake

QUALITY STAMPS DIRECT TO YOUR DOOR

Irresistibly simple, exceptionally quick and reassuringly reliable
Stanley Gibbons Mail Order service enables you to economically build your
collection from the comfort of your own home.

WE PROVIDE:

- The world's largest stocks of guaranteed quality GB material.
- Regular well produced, illustrated brochures and lists.
- Fast 48 hour order despatch.
- Free telephone advice from our team of specialists.
- A detailed register of your collecting interests.
- Exclusive special offers mailed regularly.
- Specialist 'wants list' service available.
- Over 140 years philatelic experience.

ORDER STRAIGHT FROM THIS CATALOGUE

As the world's oldest established stamp dealer, we hold comprehensive stocks.
The majority of items in this catalogue are usually available, but if we are unable to
supply, we will record your requirements and notify you, without obligation, when
they do come into stock.
**To order, complete your details and the SG numbers you require on the following
two pages, remove this section and return to:**
Stanley Gibbons Mail Order, 399 Strand, London WC2R 0LX England.

TERMS AND CONDITIONS:

1. **Minimum order £20** (excluding P&P). Minimum stamp price 30p.
2. **Please order complete sets only,** we are unable to supply individual items from sets.
3. **Please submit alternatives should your preferred requests be unavailable.** Alternatively you
   will be sent a credit note for use against your next order, if paying by cheque.
4. **All orders will be despatched within 48 hours of receipt of payment.** We cannot accept
   responsibility for delays caused in the mail.
5. **Quality of our stamps is guaranteed,** if you are dissatisfied in any way please
   return your stamps within 14 days for a full refund.

SPECIAL COMMEMORATIVE
YEAR SET OFFERS
Over the Page

COMPLETE COMMEMORATIVE YEAR SET OFFERS

Year	Unmounted Mint	Used	Presentation Pack	First Day Cover
1963	☐ £12.50	☐ £11.50	–	☐ £139.00
1964	☐ £11.00	☐ £11.00	☐ £414.00	☐ £54.00
1965	☐ £16.50	☐ £19.00	☐ £92.00	☐ £110.00
1966	☐ £7.75	☐ £9.75	☐ £96.00	☐ £54.50
1967	☐ £3.50	☐ £3.50	☐ £18.50	☐ £19.50
1968	☐ £1.75	☐ £1.75	☐ £11.25	☐ £13.50
1969	☐ £8.50	☐ £10.00	☐ £19.00	☐ £20.50
1970	☐ £4.50	☐ £5.00	☐ £16.50	☐ £12.25
1971	☐ £4.80	☐ £4.80	☐ £22.50	☐ £16.50
1972	☐ £7.00	☐ £7.25	☐ £22.50	☐ £19.75
1973	☐ £12.25	☐ £12.75	☐ £24.00	☐ £25.00
1974	☐ £5.50	☐ £5.00	☐ £14.75	☐ £14.50
1975	☐ £6.00	☐ £6.00	☐ £13.00	☐ £18.50
1976	☐ £6.00	☐ £6.00	☐ £13.00	☐ £14.50
1977	☐ £6.00	☐ £7.25	☐ £11.00	☐ £13.50
1978	☐ £6.50	☐ £6.70	☐ £11.00	☐ £10.25
1979	☐ £9.50	☐ £9.50	☐ £15.00	☐ £13.50
1980	☐ £13.00	☐ £12.75	☐ £16.00	☐ £13.50
1981	☐ £20.25	☐ £20.25	☐ £24.50	☐ £20.25
1982	☐ £17.50	☐ £16.50	☐ £23.00	☐ £17.00
1983	☐ £16.20	☐ £16.00	☐ £22.00	☐ £17.00
1984	☐ £22.50	☐ £22.50	☐ £27.50	☐ £23.50
1985	☐ £25.00	☐ £25.00	☐ £34.00	☐ £28.00
1986	☐ £28.00	☐ £27.45	☐ £36.50	☐ £35.25
1987	☐ £23.00	☐ £23.00	☐ £32.50	☐ £27.50
1988	☐ £29.50	☐ £28.75	☐ £31.00	☐ £33.00
1989	☐ £58.00	☐ £49.50	☐ £33.75	☐ £54.50
1990	☐ £60.50	☐ £55.00	☐ £37.25	☐ £63.50
1991	☐ £45.00	☐ £44.00	☐ £31.50	☐ £50.00
1992	☐ £33.25	☐ £33.25	☐ £37.25	☐ £40.00
1993	☐ £37.25	☐ £36.00	☐ £42.00	☐ £43.50
1994	☐ £33.50	☐ £33.25	☐ £43.25	☐ £42.00
1995	☐ £31.50	☐ £31.75	☐ £34.20	☐ £37.00
1996	☐ £36.25	☐ £37.25	☐ £35.00	☐ £37.50

Please tick the sets you require in the boxes provided.

CUSTOMER DETAILS

☐ **Please send me the items I have listed below**

Account No. (if valid) ☐☐☐☐☐☐☐☐☐☐

(Mr/Mrs/Miss/Ms) _____ Initial _____

Surname _____

Address _____

_____

_____

_____ Postcode _____

Telephone _____

☐ I enclose cheque/postal order made payable to **Stanley Gibbons Ltd** for: £ _____

☐ I authorise you to charge my

Mastercard ☐   Amex ☐

Diners ☐   Visa ☐

Switch ☐   Issue No. ☐☐   Switch only

Card No ☐☐☐☐☐☐☐☐☐☐☐☐☐☐☐☐☐☐☐

Expiry date ☐☐☐☐

Signature _____

ORDER FORM

Please list the items you would like supplied in the spaces below:

S.G. Cat No.	Description	Mint or Used	S.G. Cat Price	Office use only
	Please continue on a separate page			
	Plus Commemorative Year Sets from previous page			
	Allow £2.00 for postage and packing		£2.00	
	Total payable		£	

☐ Please also send me the mail order lists I have indicated on the next page

CBS1/98

FREE ILLUSTRATED GB MAIL ORDER LISTING!

- Produced twice yearly and used by thousands of collectors worldwide.
- Packed full of popular material from one of the world's largest stocks.
- Includes a number of rare and specialised items.
- Contains illustrations (many in colour), accurate descriptions and SG catalogue numbers throughout.
- Also features a number of special offers, a useful checklist and a pull out mail order form in the centre pages.
- ☐ Please send me your latest GB mail order listing.
- ☐ Please also send me mail order lists available for:
  - ☐ Australia & New Zealand   ☐ Channel Islands & Isle of Man
  - ☐ Falkland Islands

GB COLLECTORS CLUB

Our team of experts maintain detailed records of your collection and are therefore able to offer you further stamps to help you complete it. Members will receive:

- **A monthly or quarterly selection of stamps** specially selected within your own pre-set spend limit.
- **Free Stamps** worth £75 when you spend £75 per month or to the value of £50 if you spend £150 per quarter.
- **Free Album Supplements** will be sent to you each year to keep your collection up to date.
- **Regular Savings** on all the stamps we send you, generously discounted from our normal retail and catalogue prices.
- **Special Offers** on a whole range of other Stanley Gibbons catalogues, albums and accessories.
- **Interest Free Extended Payments** help you spread the cost of your stamps.

☐ Please send me further details on the GB Collectors Club

STANLEY GIBBONS *Mail Order*

Return to:
Stanley Gibbons Mail Order,
399 Strand, London WC2R 0LX, England
Tel: 0171 836 8444   Fax: 0171 836 7342

e.mail: mailorder@stangiblondon.demon.co.uk
Internet: http://www.stangib.com/

BY APPOINTMENT TO
HER MAJESTY THE QUEEN
STANLEY GIBBONS LTD
LONDON PHILATELISTS

• OUR NAME IS YOUR GUARANTEE OF QUALITY •

771 Queen Guinevere and Sir Lancelot

772 Sir Galahad

777 Alfred Hitchcock (from photo by Howard Coster)

Arthurian Legends

1985 (3 Sept.) *Phosphorised paper*

1294	**769**	17p multicoloured		50	50	☐ ☐
1295	**770**	22p multicoloured		65	75	☐ ☐
1296	**771**	31p multicoloured		1·10	1·10	☐ ☐
1297	**772**	34p multicoloured		1·10	1·25	☐ ☐
	Set of 4			3·00	3·25	☐ ☐
	First Day Cover				3·50	☐
	Presentation Pack			5·00		☐
	PHQ Cards (set of 4)			3·00	6·00	☐ ☐
	Set of 4 Gutter Pairs			6·00		☐

Nos. 1294/7 were issued on the occasion of the 500th anniversary of the printing of Sir Thomas Malory's *Morte d'Arthur.*

British Film Year

1985 (8 Oct.) *Phosphorised paper. Perf 14½*

1298	**773**	17p multicoloured		50	50	☐ ☐
1299	**774**	22p multicoloured		75	75	☐ ☐
1300	**775**	29p multicoloured		1·10	1·10	☐ ☐
1301	**776**	31p multicoloured		1·25	1·25	☐ ☐
1302	**777**	34p multicoloured		1·40	1·40	☐ ☐
	Set of 5			4·50	4·50	☐ ☐
	First Day Cover				4·75	☐
	Presentation Pack			6·50		☐
	Souvenir Book			7·50		☐
	PHQ Cards (set of 5)			3·00	6·00	☐ ☐
	Set of 5 Gutter Pairs			9·00		☐

773 Peter Sellers (from photo by Bill Brandt)

774 David Niven (from photo by Cornell Lucas)

778 Principal Boy

779 Genie

780 Dame

781 Good Fairy

775 Charlie Chaplin (from photo by Lord Snowdon)

776 Vivien Leigh (from photo by Angus McBean)

782 Pantomime Cat

Christmas. Pantomime Characters

1985 (19 Nov.) One phosphor band (12p) or phosphorised paper (others)

1303	**778**	12p multicoloured		35	30	□	□
1304	**779**	17p multicoloured		45	40	□	□
1305	**780**	22p multicoloured		70	80	□	□
1306	**781**	31p multicoloured		95	1·00	□	□
1307	**782**	34p multicoloured		1·00	1·10	□	□
		Set of 5		3·00	3·25	□	□
		First Day Cover			3·75		□
		Presentation Pack		4·50		□	
		PHQ Cards (Set of 5)		3·00	6·00	□	□
		Set of 5 Gutter Pairs		6·00		□	

Collectors Pack 1985

1985 (19 Nov.) Comprises Nos. 1272/1307

Collectors Pack		35·00	□

Post Office Yearbook

1985 Comprises Nos. 1272/1307 in hardbound book with slip case.

Yearbook		75·00	□

17 PENCE · INDUSTRY YEAR 1986

783 Light Bulb and North Sea Oil Drilling Rig (Energy)

22 PENCE · INDUSTRY YEAR 1986

784 Thermometer and Pharmaceutical Laboratory (Health)

31 PENCE · INDUSTRY YEAR 1986

785 Garden Hoe and Steel Works (Steel)

34 PENCE · INDUSTRY YEAR 1986

786 Loaf of Bread and Cornfield (Agriculture)

Industry Year

1986 (14 Jan.) Phosphorised paper. Perf $14\frac{1}{2} \times 14$

1308	**783**	17p multicoloured		45	45	□	□
1309	**784**	22p multicoloured		60	60	□	□
1310	**785**	31p multicoloured		90	90	□	□
1311	**786**	34p multicoloured		1·10	1·10	□	□
		Set of 4		2·75	2·75	□	□
		First Day Cover			3·25		□
		Presentation Pack		4·00		□	
		PHQ Cards (set of 4)		3·00	6·00	□	□
		Set of 4 Gutter Pairs		5·50		□	

787 Dr Edmond Halley as Comet

788 Giotto Spacecraft approaching Comet

789 "Twice in a Lifetime"

790 Comet orbiting Sun and Planets

Appearance of Halley's Comet

1986 (18 Feb.) Phosphorised paper.

1312	**787**	17p multicoloured		45	45	□	□
1313	**788**	22p multicoloured		70	70	□	□
1314	**789**	31p multicoloured		1·10	1·10	□	□
1315	**790**	34p multicoloured		1·10	1·10	□	□
		Set of 4		3·00	3·00	□	□
		First Day Cover			4·00		□
		Presentation Pack		4·75		□	
		PHQ Cards (set of 4)		4·00	6·00	□	□
		Set of 4 Gutter Pairs		6·00		□	

HER MAJESTY THE QUEEN
Sixtieth Birthday 17p

791 Queen Elizabeth II in 1928, 1942 and 1952

HER MAJESTY THE QUEEN
Sixtieth Birthday 17p

792 Queen Elizabeth II in 1958, 1973 and 1982

Nos. 1316/17 and 1318/19 were each printed together, *se-tenant*, in horizontal pairs throughout the sheets.

60th Birthday of Queen Elizabeth II

1986 (21 Apr.) Phosphorised paper.

1316	**791**	17p multicoloured		70	40	□	□
		a. Horiz pair.					
		Nos.1316/17		1·40	1·40	□	□
1317	**792**	17p multicoloured		70	40	□	□
1318	**791**	34p multicoloured		1·50	1·50	□	□
		a. Horiz pair.					
		Nos.1318/19		3·00	3·00	□	□
1319	**792**	34p multicoloured		1·50	1·50	□	□
		Set of 4		4·00	4·00	□	□
		First Day Cover			4·50		□
		Presentation Pack		5·00		□	
		Souvenir Book		7·50		□	
		PHQ Cards (set of 4)		3·00	6·00	□	□
		Set of 2 Gutter Blocks of 4		8·00		□	

793 Barn Owl

794 Pine Marten

795 Wild Cat

796 Natterjack Toad

Europa. Nature Conservation. Endangered Species

1986 (20 May) Phosphorised paper. Perf $14\frac{1}{2} \times 14$

1320	**793**	17p multicoloured	50	50	□	□
1321	**794**	22p multicoloured	90	75	□	□
1322	**795**	31p multicoloured	1·25	1·10	□	□
1323	**796**	34p multicoloured	1·50	1·25	□	□
		Set of 4	3·75	3·25	□	□
		First Day Cover		4·50		□
		Presentation Pack	4·50		□	
		PHQ Cards (set of 4)	3·00	6·00	□	□
		Set of 4 Gutter Pairs	7·50		□	

797 Peasants working in Fields

798 Freemen working at Town Trades

799 Knight and Retainers

800 Lord at Banquet

900th Anniversary of Domesday Book

1986 (17 June) Phosphorised paper

1324	**797**	17p multicoloured	50	50	□	□
1325	**798**	22p multicoloured	75	75	□	□
1326	**799**	31p multicoloured	1·10	1·10	□	□
1327	**800**	34p multicoloured	1·25	1·25	□	□
		Set of 4	3·25	3·25	□	□
		First Day Cover		4·00		□
		Presentation Pack	4·50		□	
		PHQ Cards (set of 4)	3·00	6·00	□	□
		Set of 4 Gutter Pairs	6·50		□	

801 Athletics

802 Rowing

803 Weightlifting

804 Rifle-Shooting

805 Hockey

Thirteenth Commonwealth Games, Edinburgh (Nos. 1328-31) and World Men's Hockey Cup, London (No. 1332)

1986 (15 July) Phosphorised paper.

1328	**801**	17p multicoloured	50	50	□	□
1329	**802**	22p multicoloured	70	70	□	□
1330	**803**	29p multicoloured	90	90	□	□
1331	**804**	31p multicoloured	1·10	1·10	□	□
1332	**805**	34p multicoloured	1·25	1·25	□	□
		Set of 5	4·00	4·00	□	□
		First Day Cover		4·25		□
		Presentation Pack	5·25		□	
		PHQ Cards (Set of 5)	4·00	6·00	□	□
		Set of 5 Gutter Pairs	8·00		□	

No. 1332 also marked the centenary of the Hockey Association.

806 Prince Andrew and Miss Sarah Ferguson 807

Royal Wedding

1986 (22 July) *One side band* (12p) *or phosphorised paper*
(17p)

1333	**806**	12p multicoloured	..	60	60	☐ ☐
1334	**807**	17p multicoloured	..	90	90	☐ ☐
		Set of 2	.. .. ..	1·50	1·50	☐ ☐
		First Day Cover	.. .. ..		2·50	☐
		Presentation Pack	..	2·00		☐
		PHQ Cards (set of 2)	..	1·50	5·00	☐ ☐
		Set of 2 Gutter Pairs	.. ..	3·00		☐

808 Stylised Cross on Ballot Paper

32nd Commonwealth Parliamentary Conference, London

1986 (19 Aug.) *Phosphorised paper. Perf* 14 × 14½.

1335	**808**	34p multicoloured	..	1·25	1·25	☐ ☐
		First Day Cover	.. .. ..		2·00	☐
		PHQ Card	.. .. ..	1·00	2·50	☐ ☐
		Gutter Pair	.. .. ..	2·50		☐

809 Lord Dowding and Hawker
Hurricane Mk I

810 Lord Tedder and Hawker
Typhoon 1B

811 Lord Trenchard and De
Havilland D.H.9A

812 Sir Arthur Harris and Avro
Type 683 Lancaster

813 Lord Portal and De
Havilland D.H.98 Mosquito

History of the Royal Air Force

1986 (16th Sept.) *Phosphorised paper. Perf* 14½ × 14.

1336	**809**	17p multicoloured	..	50	40	☐ ☐
1337	**810**	22p multicoloured	..	75	85	☐ ☐
1338	**811**	29p multicoloured	..	1·00	1·00	☐ ☐
1339	**812**	31p multicoloured	..	1·25	1·10	☐ ☐
1340	**813**	34p multicoloured	..	1·50	1·25	☐ ☐
		Set of 5	.. .. ..	4·50	4·25	☐ ☐
		First Day Cover	.. ..		5·00	☐
		Presentation Pack	..	6·00		☐
		PHQ Cards (set of 5)	..	4·00	6·50	☐ ☐
		Set of 5 Gutter Pairs	..	9·00		☐

Nos. 1336/40 were issued to celebrate the 50th anniversary
of the first R.A.F. Commands.

814 The Glastonbury Thorn

815 The Tanad Valley Plygain

816 The Hebrides Tribute

817 The Dewsbury Church Knell

818 The Hereford Boy Bishop

Christmas. Folk Customs

1986 *One phosphor band (12p, 13p) or phosphorised paper (others)*

1341	**814**	12p mult. (2 Dec.)		50	50	☐ ☐
1342		13p mult. (18 Nov.)		30	30	☐ ☐
1343	**815**	18p mult. (18 Nov.)		45	45	☐ ☐
1344	**816**	22p mult. (18 Nov.)		65	65	☐ ☐
1345	**817**	31p mult. (18 Nov.)		80	80	☐ ☐
1346	**818**	34p mult. (18 Nov.)		90	90	☐ ☐
		Set of 6		3·25	3·25	☐ ☐
		First Day Covers (2)			5·25	☐
		Presentation Pack (Nos. 1342/6)	5·00			☐
		PHQ Cards (set of 5) (Nos. 1342/6)		3·00	6·00	☐ ☐
		Set of 6 Gutter Pairs		6·50		☐

Collectors Pack 1986

1986 (18 Nov.) Comprises Nos. 1308/40, 1342/6

	Collectors Pack	35·00	☐

Post Office Yearbook

1986 Comprises Nos. 1308/40, 1342/6 in hardbound book with slip case.

	Yearbook	65·00	☐

819 North American Blanket Flower

820 Globe Thistle

821 Echeveria

822 Autumn Crocus

Flower Photographs by Alfred Lammer

1987 (20 Jan) *Phosphorised paper. Perf 14½ × 14*

1347	**819**	18p multicoloured		50	50	☐ ☐
1348	**820**	22p multicoloured		80	70	☐ ☐
1349	**821**	31p multicoloured		1·25	1·10	☐ ☐
1350	**822**	34p multicoloured		1·40	1·25	☐ ☐
		Set of 4		3·50	3·25	☐ ☐
		First Day Cover			4·25	☐
		Presentation Pack		4·75		☐
		PHQ Cards (set of 4)		3·00	6·00	☐ ☐
		Set of 4 Gutter Pairs		7·00		☐

823 The Principia Mathematica

824 Motion of Bodies in Ellipses

825 Optick Treatise

826 The System of the World

300th Anniversary of The Principia Mathematica by Sir Isaac Newton

1987 (24 Mar) *Phosphorised paper.*

1351	**823**	18p multicoloured		50	50	☐ ☐
1352	**824**	22p multicoloured		70	70	☐ ☐
1353	**825**	31p multicoloured		1·10	1·10	☐ ☐
1354	**826**	34p multicoloured		1·25	1·25	☐ ☐
		Set of 4		3·25	3·25	☐ ☐
		First Day Cover			3·50	☐
		Presentation Pack		4·50		☐
		PHQ Cards (set of 4)		3·00	6·00	☐ ☐
		Set of 4 Gutter Pairs		6·50		☐

For full information on all future British issues, collectors should write to the British Post Office Philatelic Bureau, 20 Brandon Street, Edinburgh EH3 5TT

827 Willis Faber and Dumas
Building. Ipswich

828 Pompidou Centre. Paris

829 Staatsgalerie. Stuttgart

830 European Investment
Bank. Luxembourg

Europa. British Architects in Europe

1987 (12 MAY) *Phosphorised paper.*

1355	827	18p multicoloured		50	50	☐ ☐
1356	828	22p multicoloured		70	70	☐ ☐
1357	829	31p multicoloured		1·10	1·10	☐ ☐
1358	830	34p multicoloured		1·25	1·25	☐ ☐
		Set of 4		3·25	3·25	☐ ☐
		First Day Cover			3·50	☐
		Presentation Pack		4·50		☐
		PHQ Cards (set of 4)		3·00	6·00	☐ ☐
		Set of 4 Gutter Pairs		6·50		☐

831 Brigade Members
with Ashford
Litter. 1887

832 Bandaging Blitz
Victim. 1940

833 Volunteer with
fainting Girl.
1965

834 Transport of
Transplant Organ by
Air Wing. 1987

Centenary of St. John Ambulance Brigade

1987 (16 JUNE) *Phosphorised paper. Perf 14 × 14½*

1359	831	18p multicoloured		50	50	☐ ☐
1360	832	22p multicoloured		65	65	☐ ☐
1361	833	31p multicoloured		1·10	1·10	☐ ☐
1362	834	34p multicoloured		1·10	1·10	☐ ☐
		Set of 4		3·00	3·00	☐ ☐
		First Day Cover			3·50	☐
		Presentation Pack		4·50		☐
		PHQ Cards (set of 4)		3·00	6·00	☐ ☐
		Set of 4 Gutter Pairs		6·00		☐

835 Arms of the Lord
Lyon King of Arms

836 Scottish Heraldic
Banner of Prince Charles

837 Arms of Royal
Scottish Academy of
Painting. Sculpture
and Architecture

838 Arms of Royal
Society of Edinburgh

300th Anniversary of Revival of Order of the Thistle

1987 (21 JULY) *Phosphorised paper. Perf 14½*

1363	835	18p multicoloured		50	50	☐ ☐
1364	836	22p multicoloured		65	65	☐ ☐
1365	837	31p multicoloured		1·10	1·10	☐ ☐
1366	838	34p multicoloured		1·10	1·10	☐ ☐
		Set of 4		3·00	3·00	☐ ☐
		First Day Cover			4·25	☐
		Presentation Pack		4·50		☐
		PHQ Cards (set of 4)		3·00	6·00	☐ ☐
		Set of 4 Gutter Pairs		6 00		☐

839 Crystal Palace, Monarch of the Glen (Landseer) and Grace Darling

840 Great Eastern, Beeton's Book of Household Management and Prince Albert

841 Albert Memorial, Ballot Box and Disraeli

842 Diamond Jubilee Emblem, Morse Key and Newspaper Placard for Relief of Mafeking

150th Anniversary of Queen Victoria's Accession

1987 (8 SEPT) *Phosphorised paper.*

1367	**839**	18p multicoloured		50	50	☐ ☐
1368	**840**	22p multicoloured		75	75	☐ ☐
1369	**841**	31p multicoloured		1·10	1·10	☐ ☐
1370	**842**	34p multicoloured		1·25	1·25	☐ ☐
		Set of 4		3·25	3·25	☐ ☐
		First Day Cover			4·25	☐
		Presentation Pack		4·75		☐
		PHQ Cards (set of 4)		3·00	6·00	☐ ☐
		Set of 4 Gutter Pairs		6·50		☐

843 Pot by Bernard Leach

844 Pot by Elizabeth Fritsch

845 Pot by Lucie Rie

846 Pot by Hans Coper

Studio Pottery

1987 (13 OCT) *Phosphorised paper. Perf 14½ × 14*

1371	**843**	18p multicoloured		50	50	☐ ☐
1372	**844**	26p multicoloured		70	70	☐ ☐
1373	**845**	31p multicoloured		1·10	1·10	☐ ☐
1374	**846**	34p multicoloured		1·25	1·25	☐ ☐
		Set of 4		3·25	3·25	☐ ☐
		First Day Cover			3·50	☐
		Presentation Pack		4·50		☐
		PHQ Cards (set of 4)		3·00	6·00	☐ ☐
		Set of 4 Gutter Pairs		6·50		☐

Nos. 1371/4 also mark the birth centenary of Bernard Leach, the potter.

847 Decorating the Christmas tree

848 Waiting for Father Christmas

849 Sleeping Child and Father Christmas in Sleigh

850 Child reading

851 Child playing Flute and Snowman

Christmas

1987 (17 Nov) *One phosphor band (13p) or phosphorised paper (others)*

1375	**847**	13p multicoloured		30	30	☐ ☐
1376	**848**	18p multicoloured		50	50	☐ ☐
1377	**849**	26p multicoloured		75	75	☐ ☐
1378	**850**	31p multicoloured		95	1·10	☐ ☐
1379	**851**	34p multicoloured		1·10	1·25	☐ ☐
		Set of 5		3·25	3·50	☐ ☐
		First Day Cover			4·25	☐
		Presentation Pack		4·50		☐
		PHQ Cards (set of 5)		3·00	6·00	☐ ☐
		Set of 5 Gutter Pairs		6·50		☐

1987 (17 Nov.) *Comprises Nos. 1347/79*

Collectors Pack	..	38·00	☐

Post Office Yearbook

1987 *Comprises Nos. 1347/79 in hardbound book with slip case*

Yearbook	.. ..	40·00	☐

852 Bull-rout (Jonathan Couch)

853 Yellow Waterlily (Major Joshua Swatkin)

854 Whistling ("Bewick's") Swan (Edward Lear)

855 *Morchella esculenta* (James Sowerby)

Bicentenary of Linnean Society. Archive Illustrations

1988 (19 Jan.) *Phosphorised paper*

1380	852	18p multicoloured	..	60	45	☐ ☐
1381	853	26p multicoloured	..	80	70	☐ ☐
1382	854	31p multicoloured	..	1·25	1·10	☐ ☐
1383	855	34p multicoloured	..	1·25	1·10	☐ ☐
		Set of 4	.. ..	3·50	3·00	☐ ☐
		First Day Cover	..		3·50	☐
		Presentation Pack	..	4·50		☐
		PHQ Cards (set of 4)		3·00	6·00	☐ ☐
		Set of 4 Gutter Pairs	.. ..	7·00		☐

856 Revd William Morgan (Bible translator, 1588)

857 William Salesbury (New Testament translator, 1567)

858 Bishop Richard Davies (New Testament translator, 1567)

859 Bishop Richard Parry (editor of Revised Welsh Bible, 1620)

400th Anniversary of Welsh Bible

1988 (1 Mar.) *Phosphorised paper. Perf* $14\frac{1}{2} \times 14$

1384	856	18p multicoloured	..	45	45	☐ ☐
1385	857	26p multicoloured	..	70	70	☐ ☐
1386	858	31p multicoloured	..	1·10	1·10	☐ ☐
1387	859	34p multicoloured	..	1·10	1·10	☐ ☐
		Set of 4	.. ..	3·00	3·00	☐ ☐
		First Day Cover	.. ..		4·00	☐
		Presentation Pack	..	4·50		☐
		PHQ Cards (set of 4)		3·00	6·00	☐ ☐
		Set of 4 Gutter Pairs	.. ..	6·00		☐

860 Gymnastics (Centenary of British Amateur Gymnastics Association)

861 Downhill Skiing (Ski Club of Great Britain)

862 Tennis (Centenary of Lawn Tennis Association)

863 Football (Centenary of Football League)

Sports Organizations

1988 (22 Mar.) *Phosphorised paper. Perf* 14½

1388	**860**	18p multicoloured	45	45	☐ ☐
1389	**861**	26p multicoloured	70	70	☐ ☐
1390	**862**	31p multicoloured	1·10	1·10	☐ ☐
1391	**863**	34p multicoloured	1·10	1·10	☐ ☐
		Set of 4	3·00	3·00	☐ ☐
		First Day Cover		4·00	☐
		Presentation Pack	4·50		☐
		PHQ Cards (set of 4)	2·25	5·00	☐ ☐
		Set of 4 Gutter Pairs	6·00		☐

864 *Mallard* and Mailbags on Pick-up Arms

865 Loading Transatlantic Mail on Liner *Queen Elizabeth*

866 Glasgow Tram No. 1173 and Pillar Box

867 Imperial Airways Handley Page H.P.45 *Horatius* and Airmail Van

Europa. Transport and Mail Services in 1930's

1988 (10 May) *Phosphorised paper*

1392	**864**	18p multicoloured	50	50	☐ ☐
1393	**865**	26p multicoloured	80	80	☐ ☐
1394	**866**	31p multicoloured	1·10	1·10	☐ ☐
1395	**867**	34p multicoloured	1·25	1·25	☐ ☐
		Set of 4	3·25	3·25	☐ ☐
		First Day Cover		3·50	☐
		Presentation Pack	4·50		☐
		PHQ Cards (set of 4)	2·00	5·00	☐ ☐
		Set of 4 Gutter Pairs	6·50		☐

868 Early Settler and Sailing Clipper

869 Queen Elizabeth II with British and Australian Parliament Buildings

870 W. G. Grace (cricketer) and Tennis Racquet

871 Shakespeare, John Lennon (entertainer) and Sydney Landmarks

Nos. 1396/7 and 1398/9 were each printed together, *se-tenant*, in horizontal pairs throughout the sheets, each pair showing a background design of the Australian flag.

Bicentenary of Australian Settlement

1988 (21 June) *Phosphorised paper. Perf* 14½

1396	**868**	18p multicoloured	60	60	☐ ☐
		a. Horiz pair. Nos. 1396/7	1·25	1·25	☐ ☐
1397	**869**	18p multicoloured	60	60	☐ ☐
1398	**870**	34p multicoloured	1·10	1·10	☐ ☐
		a. Horiz pair. Nos. 1398/9	2·40	2·40	☐ ☐
1399	**871**	34p multicoloured	1·10	1·10	☐ ☐
		Set of 4	3·25	3·25	☐ ☐
		First Day Cover		3·50	☐
		Presentation Pack	4·50		☐
		Souvenir Book	6·00		☐
		PHQ Cards (set of 4)	2·00	5·00	☐ ☐
		Set of 2 Gutter Blocks of 4	6·50		☐

Stamps in similar designs were also issued by Australia. These are included in the Souvenir Book.

872 Spanish Galeasse off The Lizard

873 English Fleet leaving Plymouth

874 Engagement off Isle of Wight

875 Attack of English Fire-ships, Calais

876 Armada in Storm, North Sea

Nos. 1400/4 were printed together, *se-tenant*, in horizontal strips of 5 throughout the sheet, forming a composite design.

400th Anniversary of Spanish Armada

1988 (19 JULY) *Phosphorised paper*

1400	**872**	18p multicoloured		65	65	☐ ☐
		a. Horiz strip of 5.				
		Nos. 1400/4		2·75	2·75	☐ ☐
1401	**873**	18p multicoloured		65	65	☐ ☐
1402	**874**	18p multicoloured		65	65	☐ ☐
1403	**875**	18p multicoloured		65	65	☐ ☐
1404	**876**	18p multicoloured		65	65	☐ ☐
		Set of 5		2·75	2·75	☐ ☐
		First Day Cover			3·25	☐
		Presentation Pack		4·00		☐
		PHQ Cards (set of 5)		2·50	5·50	☐ ☐
		Gutter Block of 10		5·50		☐

877 "The Owl and the Pussy-cat"

878 "Edward Lear as a Bird" (self-portrait)

879 "Cat" (from alphabet book)

880 "There was a Young Lady whose Bonnet..." (limerick)

Death Centenary of Edward Lear (artist and author)

1988 (6–27 SEPT.) *Phosphorised paper*

1405	**877**	19p black, pale cream and carmine		50	50	☐ ☐
1406	**878**	27p black, pale cream and yellow		65	80	☐ ☐
1407	**879**	32p black, pale cream and emerald		1·10	1·10	☐ ☐
1408	**880**	35p black, pale cream and blue		1·10	1·25	☐ ☐
		Set of 4		3·00	3·25	☐ ☐
		First Day Cover			4·00	☐
		Presentation Pack		4·50		☐
		PHQ Cards (set of 4)		2·00	5·00	☐ ☐
		Set of 4 Gutter Pairs		6·00		☐
MS1409		122 × 90 mm. Nos. 1405/8		8·00	7·00	☐ ☐
		First Day Cover (27 Sept.)			7·00	☐

No. **MS**1409 was sold at £1·35, the premium being used for the "Stamp World London 90" International Stamp Exhibition.

881 Carrickfergus Castle

882 Caernarvon Castle

883 Edinburgh Castle

884 Windsor Castle

1988 (18 OCT.) *Ordinary paper*

1410	**881**	£1 deep green		3·00	50	☐ ☐
1411	**882**	£1·50 maroon		4·50	1·25	☐ ☐
1412	**883**	£2 indigo		6·50	1·75	☐ ☐
1413	**884**	£5 deep brown		15·00	3·50	☐ ☐
		Set of 4		26·00	6·25	☐ ☐
		First Day Cover			45·00	☐
		Presentation Pack		28·00		☐
		Set of 4 Gutter Pairs		50·00		☐

For similar designs, but with silhouette Queen's head see Nos. 1611/14 and 1993/6.

885 Journey to Bethlehem

886 Shepherds and Star

887 Three Wise Men

888 Nativity

889 The Annunciation

Christmas

1988 (15 Nov.) *One phosphor band* (14p) *or phosphorised paper* (others)

1414	**885**	14p multicoloured	..	35	35	☐ ☐
1415	**886**	19p multicoloured	..	40	45	☐ ☐
1416	**887**	27p multicoloured	..	70	70	☐ ☐
1417	**888**	32p multicoloured	..	90	1·00	☐ ☐
1418	**889**	35p multicoloured	..	1·00	1·10	☐ ☐
		Set of 5	..	3·00	3·25	☐ ☐
		First Day Cover	.. ..		4·25	☐
		Presentation Pack	..	4·25		☐
		PHQ Cards (set of 5)	..	2·50	5·25	☐ ☐
		Set of 5 Gutter Pairs	..	6·00		☐

Collectors Pack 1988

1988 (15 Nov.) *Comprises Nos.* 1380/1408, 1414/18

	Collectors Pack	.. ..	32·00	☐

Post Office Yearbook

1988 *Comprises Nos.* 1380/1404, **MS**1409, 1414/18 *in hardbound book with slip case*

Yearbook	.. .. ..	40·00	☐

890 Atlantic Puffin

891 Avocet

892 Oystercatcher

893 Northern Gannet

Centenary of Royal Society for the Protection of Birds

1989 (17 Jan.) *Phosphorised paper*

1419	**890**	19p multicoloured	..	45	45	☐ ☐
1420	**891**	27p multicoloured	..	1·25	1·10	☐ ☐
1421	**892**	32p multicoloured	..	1·25	1·10	☐ ☐
1422	**893**	35p multicoloured	..	1·50	1·25	☐ ☐
		Set of 4	.. ..	4·00	3·50	☐ ☐
		First Day Cover	..		4·50	☐
		Presentation Pack	..	4·50		☐
		PHQ Cards (set of 4)	..	2·50	5·00	☐ ☐
		Set of 4 Gutter Pairs	..	8·00		☐

894 Rose

895 Cupid

896 Yachts

897 Fruit

898 Teddy Bear

Nos. 1423/7 were printed together, *se-tenant*, in horizontal strips of five, two such strips forming the booklet pane with twelve half stamp-size labels.

Greetings Booklet Stamps

1989 (31 JAN.) *Phosphorised paper*

1423	**894**	19p multicoloured		6·25	4·50	☐ ☐
		a. *Booklet pane.*				
		Nos. 1423/7 × 2		55·00		☐
1424	**895**	19p multicoloured		6·25	4·50	☐ ☐
1425	**896**	19p multicoloured		6·25	4·50	☐ ☐
1426	**897**	19p multicoloured		6·25	4·50	☐ ☐
1427	**898**	19p multicoloured		6·25	4·50	☐ ☐
		Set of 5		28·00	20·00	☐ ☐
		First Day Cover			20·00	☐

899 Fruit and Vegetables

900 Meat Products

901 Dairy Produce

902 Cereal Products

Food and Farming Year

1989 (7 MAR.) *Phosphorised paper. Perf* 14 × 14½

1428	**899**	19p multicoloured		50	50	☐ ☐
1429	**900**	27p multicoloured		80	80	☐ ☐
1430	**901**	32p multicoloured		1·10	1·10	☐ ☐
1431	**902**	35p multicoloured		1·25	1·25	☐ ☐
		Set of 4		3·25	3·25	☐ ☐
		First Day Cover			4·25	☐
		Presentation Pack		4·50		☐
		PHQ Cards (set of 4)		2·00	5·00	☐ ☐
		Set of 4 Gutter Pairs		6·50		☐

903 Mortar Board (150th Anniv of Public Education in England)

904 Cross on Ballot Paper (3rd Direct Elections to European Parliament)

905 Posthorn (26th Postal, Telegraph and Telephone International Congress Brighton)

906 Globe (Inter-Parliamentary Union Centenary Conference, London)

Nos. 1432/3 and 1434/5 were each printed together, *se-tenant*, in horizontal pairs throughout the sheets.

Anniversaries

1989 (11 APR.) *Phosphorised paper. Perf* 14 × 14½

1432	**903**	19p multicoloured		1·25	1·25	☐ ☐
		a. *Horiz pair.*				
		Nos. 1432/3		2·50	2·50	☐ ☐
1433	**904**	19p multicoloured		1·25	1·25	☐ ☐
1434	**905**	35p multicoloured		1·75	1·75	☐ ☐
		a. *Horiz pair.*				
		Nos. 1434/5		3·50	3·50	☐ ☐
1435	**906**	35p multicoloured		1·75	1·75	☐ ☐
		Set of 4		5·50	5·50	☐ ☐
		First Day Cover			6·00	☐
		Presentation Pack		6·50		☐
		PHQ Cards (set of 4)		2·00	7·00	☐ ☐
		Set of 2 Gutter Strips of 4		11·00		☐

907 Toy Train and Airplane

908 Building Bricks

909 Dice and Board Games

910 Toy Robot, Boat and Doll's House

Europa. Games and Toys

1989 (16 May) *Phosphorised paper*

1436	**907**	19p multicoloured	..	50	50	☐	☐
1437	**908**	27p multicoloured	..	90	90	☐	☐
1438	**909**	32p multicoloured	..	1·25	1·25	☐	☐
1439	**910**	35p multicoloured	..	1·40	1·40	☐	☐
		Set of 4	..	3·50	3·50	☐	☐
		First Day Cover	..		4·25		☐
		Presentation Pack	.. ..	4·50		☐	
		PHQ Cards (set of 4)	.. ..	2·00	5·00	☐	☐
		Set of 4 Gutter Pairs	.. ..	7·00		☐	

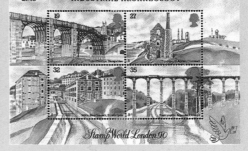

£1·40   INDUSTRIAL ARCHAEOLOGY

Stamp World London 90

915

Industrial Archaeology

1989 (4–25 July) *Phosphorised paper*

1440	**911**	19p multicoloured		50	50	☐	☐
1441	**912**	27p multicoloured	..	80	80	☐	☐
1442	**913**	32p multicoloured		1·00	1·00	☐	☐
1443	**914**	35p multicoloured	..	1·10	1·10	☐	☐
		Set of 4	..	3·00	3·00	☐	☐
		First Day Cover	..		4·25		☐
		Presentation Pack		4·50		☐	
		PHQ Cards (set of 4)		2·00	5·00	☐	☐
		Set of 4 Gutter Pairs		6·50		☐	
MS1444	122 × 90 mm. **915** As Nos.						
	1440/3 but designs horizontal			6·50	5·50	☐	☐
	First Day Cover (25 July)				5·50		☐

No. **MS**1444 was sold at £1.40, the premium being used for the "Stamp World London 90" International Stamp Exhibition.

911 Ironbridge, Shropshire

912 Tin Mine, St. Agnes Head, Cornwall

916

917

913 Cotton Mills, New Lanark, Strathclyde

914 Pontcysyllte Aqueduct, Clwyd

Booklet Stamps

1989 (22 Aug.)–**92**

(a) Printed in photogravure by Harrison and Sons. Perf 15 × 14

1445	**916**	(2nd) bright blue (1 centre band)	.. ..	70	35	☐	☐
1446		(2nd bright blue (1 side band) (20.3.90)	.. ..	2·25	2·25	☐	☐
1447	**917**	(1st) black (phosphorised paper		1·25	50	☐	☐
1448		(1st brownish black (2 bands) (20.3.90)	.. ..	2·25	2·25	☐	☐

(b) Printed in lithography by Walsall. Perf 14

1449	**916**	(2nd) bright blue (1 centre band)	.. .. ..	1·00	1·00	☐	☐
1450	**917**	(1st) black (2 bands)	.. ..	1·75	1·50	☐	☐

(c) Printed in lithography by Questa. Perf 15 × 14

1451 **916**	(2nd) bright blue (1 centre band) (19.9.89)	85	85	□	□
1451*a*	(2nd) bright blue (1 side band) (25.2.92)	1·25	1·25	□	□
1452 **917**	(1st) black (phosphorised paper) (19.9.89)	1·25	1·25	□	□
	First Day Cover (Nos. 1445, 1447)		3·50		□

For similar stamps showing changed colours see Nos. 1511/16 and for those with elliptical perforations Nos. 1663*a*/6 and 1979.

No. 1451*a* exists with the phosphor band at the left or right of the stamp.

918 Snowflake (× 10)

919 *Calliphora erythrocephala* (fly) (× 5)

920 Blood Cells (× 500)

921 Microchip (× 600)

150th Anniversary of Royal Microscopical Society

1989 (5 SEPT.) *Phosphorised paper. Perf* $14\frac{1}{2}$ × 14

1453	**918**	19p multicoloured		50	50	□ □
1454	**919**	27p multicoloured		85	85	□ □
1455	**920**	32p multicoloured		1·25	1·25	□ □
1456	**921**	35p multicoloured		1·40	1·40	□ □
		Set of 4		3·50	3·50	□ □
		First Day Cover			4·25	□
		Presentation Pack		4·00		□
		PHQ Cards (set of 4)		2·00	5·00	□ □
		Set of 4 Gutter Pairs		7·00		□

922 Royal Mail Coach

923 Escort of Blues and Royals

924 Lord Mayor's Coach

925 Coach Team passing St Paul's

926 Blues and Royals Drum Horse

Nos. 1457/61 were printed together, *se-tenant*, in horizontal strips of 5 throughout the sheet, forming a composite design.

Lord Mayor's Show, London

1989 (17 OCT.) *Phosphorised paper*

1457	**922**	20p multicoloured		75	80	□ □
		a. Horiz strip of 5 Nos. 1457/61		3·25	3·50	□ □
1458	**923**	20p multicoloured		75	80	□ □
1459	**924**	20p multicoloured		75	80	□ □
1460	**925**	20p multicoloured		75	80	□ □
1461	**926**	20p multicoloured		75	80	□ □
		Set of 5		3·25	3·50	□ □
		First Day Cover			3·75	□
		Presentation Pack		4·50		□
		PHQ Cards (set of 5)		2·50	5·00	□ □
		Gutter Strip of 10		6·50		□

Nos. 1457/61 commemorate the 800th anniversary of the installation of the first Lord Mayor of London.

927 14th-century Peasants from Stained-glass Window

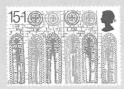

928 Arches and Roundels, West Front

929 Octagon Tower

930 Arcade from West Transept

931 Triple Arch from West Front

932 Queen Victoria and Queen Elizabeth II

Christmas. 800th Anniversary of Ely Cathedral

1989 (14 Nov.) *One phosphor band (Nos. 1462/3) or phosphorised paper (others)*

1462	**927**	15p gold, silver and blue	35	35 ☐ ☐
1463	**928**	15p + 1p gold, silver and blue	50	40 ☐ ☐
1464	**929**	20p + 1p gold, silver and rosine	60	50 ☐ ☐
1465	**930**	34p + 1p gold, silver and emerald	1·25	1·40 ☐ ☐
1466	**931**	37p + 1p gold, silver and yellow-olive	1·25	1·40 ☐ ☐
		Set of 5	3·50	3·50 ☐ ☐
		First Day Cover		4·00 ☐
		Presentation Pack	4·50	☐
		PHQ Cards (set of 5)	2·50	5·00 ☐ ☐
		Set of 5 Gutter Pairs	7·00	☐

Collectors Pack 1989

1989 (14 Nov.) *Comprises Nos. 1419/22, 1428/43 and 1453/66*

	Collectors Pack	35·00	☐

Post Office Yearbook

1989 (14 Nov.) *Comprises Nos. 1419/22, 1428/44 and 1453/66 in hardback book with slip case.*

	Yearbook	40·00	☐

150th Anniversary of the Penny Black

1990 (10 JAN.–17 APR.)

(a) Printed in photogravure by Harrison and Sons. Perf 15 × 14

1467	**932**	15p bright blue (1 centre band)	50	50 ☐ ☐
1468		15p bright blue (1 side band) (30 Jan)	70	80 ☐ ☐
1469		20p brownish black and cream (phosphorised paper)	75	75 ☐ ☐
1470		20p brnish blk & cream (2 bands) (30 Jan)	1·75	1·50 ☐ ☐
1471		29p deep mauve (phosphorised paper)	1·25	1·25 ☐ ☐
1472		29p deep mauve (2 bands) (20 Mar)	8·00	8·00 ☐ ☐
1473		34p deep bluish grey (phosphorised paper)	1·50	1·25 ☐ ☐
1474		37p rosine (phosphorised paper)	1·50	1·50 ☐ ☐
		Set of 5 (Nos. 1467, 1469, 1471, 1473/4)	5·25	5·25 ☐ ☐
		First Day Cover (Nos. 1467, 1469, 1471, 1473/4)		5·00 ☐
		Presentation Pack (Nos. 1467, 1469, 1471, 1473/4)	5·75	☐

(b) Litho Walsall. Perf 14 (30 Jan)

1475	**932**	15p bright blue (1 centre band)	90	70 ☐ ☐
1476		20p brnish blk & cream (phosphorised paper)	1·25	80 ☐ ☐

(c) Litho Questa. Perf 15 × 14 (17 Apr)

1477	**932**	15p bright blue (1 centre band)	1·50	1·50 ☐ ☐
1478		20p brnish black (phosphorised paper)	1·50	1·50 ☐ ☐

No. 1468 exists with the phosphor band at the left or right of the stamp.

933 Kitten

934 Rabbit

935 Duckling

936 Puppy

150th Anniversary of Royal Society for Prevention of Cruelty to Animals

1990 (23 Jan.) *Phosphorised paper. Perf* 14 × 14½.

1479	**933**	20p multicoloured	..	65	70	☐	☐
1480	**934**	29p multicoloured	..	1·25	1·10	☐	☐
1481	**935**	34p multicoloured	..	1·50	1·25	☐	☐
1482	**936**	37p multicoloured	..	1·60	1·40	☐	☐
		Set of 4	.. .. ..	4·50	4·00	☐	☐
		First Day Cover	.. ..		4·25		☐
		Presentation Pack	..	5·00		☐	
		PHQ Cards (set of 4)	.. ..	2·50	5·50	☐	☐
		Set of 4 Gutter Pairs	.. ..	9·00		☐	

937 Teddy Bear

938 Dennis the Menace

939 Punch

940 Cheshire Cat

941 The Man in the Moon

942 The Laughing Policeman

943 Clown

944 Mona Lisa

945 Queen of Hearts

946 Stan Laurel (comedian)

T **937**/46 were printed together, *se-tenant,* in booklet panes of 10.

Greetings Booklet Stamps. "Smiles"

1990 (6 Feb.) *Two phosphor bands*

1483	**937**	20p multicoloured	..	3·25	2·50	☐	☐
		a. Booklet pane.					
		Nos. 1483/92	..	28·00		☐	
1484	**938**	20p multicoloured	..	3·25	2·50	☐	☐
1485	**939**	20p multicoloured	..	3·25	2·50	☐	☐
1486	**940**	20p multicoloured	..	3·25	2·50	☐	☐
1487	**941**	20p multicoloured	..	3·25	2·50	☐	☐
1488	**942**	20p multicoloured	..	3·25	2·50	☐	☐
1489	**943**	20p multicoloured	..	3·25	2·50	☐	☐
1490	**944**	20p multicoloured	..	3·25	2·50	☐	☐
1491	**945**	20p multicoloured	..	3·25	2·50	☐	☐
1492	**946**	20p gold and grey-black	..	3·25	2·50	☐	☐
		Set of 10	.. ..	28·00	22·00	☐	☐
		First Day Cover	.. ..		24·00		☐

For those designs with the face value expressed as "1st" see Nos. 1550/9.

947 Alexandra Palace ("Stamp World London 90" Exhibition)

948 Glasgow School of Art

949 British Philatelic Bureau, Edinburgh

950 Templeton Carpet Factory, Glasgow

Europa (Nos. 1493 and 1495) and "Glasgow 1990 European City of Culture" (Nos. 1494 and 1496)

1990 (6 MAR.) *Phosphorised paper*

1493	947	20p multicoloured	..	50	50	☐	☐
1494	948	20p multicoloured	..	50	50	☐	☐
1495	949	29p multicoloured	..	1·10	1·10	☐	☐
1496	950	37p multicoloured	..	1·25	1·25	☐	☐
		Set of 4		3·00	3·00	☐	☐
		First Day Cover	.. ..		4·25		☐
		Presentation Pack		4·00		☐	
		PHQ Cards (set of 4)	..	2·50	5·25	☐	☐
		Set of 4 Gutter Pairs	.. ..	6·00		☐	

951 Export Achievement Award

952 Technological Achievement Award

Nos. 1497/8 and 1499/500 were each printed together, *se-tenant*, in horizontal pairs throughout the sheets.

25th Anniversary of Queen's Awards for Export and Technology

1990 (10 APR.) *Phosphorised paper. Perf* 14 × 14½.

1497	951	20p multicoloured	..	75	75	☐	☐
		a. Horiz pair.					
		Nos. 1497/8 ..	..	1·50	1·50	☐	☐
1498	952	20p multicoloured	..	75	75	☐	☐
1499	951	37p multicoloured	..	1·40	1·40	☐	☐
		a. Horiz pair.					
		Nos. 1499/500	..	2·75	2·75	☐	☐
1500	952	37p multicoloured	..	1·40	1·40	☐	☐
		Set of 4	..	3·75	3·75	☐	
		First Day Cover			4·50		☐
		Presentation Pack	.. ..	4·00		☐	
		PHQ Cards (set of 4)	..	2·50	5·25	☐	
		Set of 2 Gutter Strips of 4		7·50		☐	

953

"Stamp World 90" International Stamp Exhibition, London

1990 (3 MAY) *Sheet* 122 × 90 *mm. Phosphorised paper*

MS1501	953	20p. brownish black and cream	4·25	4·25	☐ ☐
		First Day Cover		5·00	☐
		Souvenir Book (Nos. 1467, 1469, 1471, 1473/4 and MS1501)	17·00		☐

No. **MS**1501 was sold at £1, the premium being used for the exhibition.

954 Cycad and Sir Joseph Banks Building

955 Stone Pine and Princess of Wales Conservatory

956 Willow Tree and Palm House

957 Cedar Tree and Pagoda

150th Anniversary of Kew Gardens

1990 (5 JUNE) *Phosphorised paper*

1502	954	20p multicoloured	..	50	50	☐	☐
1503	955	29p multicoloured	..	80	80	☐	☐

1504	**956**	34p multicoloured	..	1·10	1·25	☐	☐
1505	**957**	37p multicoloured	..	1·25	1·40	☐	☐
		Set of 4	.. ..	3·25	3·50	☐	☐
		First Day Cover	.. ..		4·50		☐
		Presentation Pack	..	4·00		☐	
		PHQ Cards (set of 4)		2·50	5·00	☐	☐
		Set of 4 Gutter Pairs		6·50		☐	

958 Thomas Hardy and Clyffe Clump, Dorset

150th Birth Anniversary of Thomas Hardy (author)

1990 (10 July) Phosphorised paper

1506	**958**	20p multicoloured	..	75	75	☐	☐
		First Day Cover	.. .. ..		2·00		☐
		Presentation Pack	..	1·75		☐	
		PHQ Card	.. .. ..	75	2·00	☐	☐
		Gutter Pair	.. .. ..	1·50		☐	

959 Queen Elizabeth the Queen Mother

960 Queen Elizabeth

961 Elizabeth, Duchess of York

962 Lady Elizabeth Bowes-Lyon

90th Birthday of Queen Elizabeth the Queen Mother

1990 (2 Aug.) Phosphorised paper

1507	**959**	20p multicoloured		70	70	☐	☐
1508	**960**	29p silver, indigo and grey-blue		1·00	1·00	☐	☐

1509	**961**	34p multicoloured		1·50	1·50	☐	☐
1510	**962**	37p silver, sepia and stone	..	1·75	1·75	☐	☐
		Set of 4	.. .. ..	4·50	4·50	☐	☐
		First Day Cover	.. ..		4·75		☐
		Presentation Pack	..	4·75		☐	
		PHQ Cards (set of 4)	..	2·50	5·50	☐	☐
		Set of 4 Gutter Pairs ..	..	9·00		☐	

Booklet Stamps

1990 (7 Aug) -**92** As Types **916/17**, but colours changed

(a) Photo Harrison, Perf 15 × 14

1511	**916**	(2nd) dp blue (1 centre band)	..	90	90	☐	☐
1512	**917**	(1st) brt orge-red (phosphorised paper)	..	80	80	☐	☐

(b) Litho Questa. Perf 15 × 14

1513	**916**	(2nd) dp blue (1 centre band)	..	1·60	1·60	☐	☐
1514	**917**	(1st) brt orge-red (phosphorised paper)	..	75	75	☐	☐
1514a		(1st) brt orange-red (2 bands) (25.2.92)	..	1·25	1·25	☐	☐

(c) Litho Walsall. Perf 14

1515	**916**	(2nd) dp blue (1 centre band)	..	60	60	☐	☐
1516	**917**	(1st) brt orge-red (phosphorised paper)	..	60	60	☐	☐
		c. Perf 13	..	2·25	2·25	☐	☐
		First Day Cover (Nos. 1515/16)	.. ..		3·50		☐

For similar stamps with elliptical perforations see Nos. 1663a/6.

963 Victoria Cross

964 George Cross

965 Distinguished Service Cross and Distinguished Service Medal

966 Military Cross and Military Medal

967 Distinguished Flying Cross and Distinguished Flying Medal

Gallantry Awards

1990 (11 SEPT.) *Phosphorised paper*

1517	**963**	20p multicoloured	80	80	☐	☐
1518	**964**	20p multicoloured	80	80	☐	☐
1519	**965**	20p multicoloured	80	80	☐	☐
1520	**966**	20p multicoloured	80	80	☐	☐
1521	**967**	20p multicoloured	80	80	☐	☐
		Set of 5	3·50	3·50	☐	☐
		First Day Cover		3·75		☐
		Presentation Pack	4·00		☐	
		PHQ Cards (set of 5)	3·00	5·50	☐	☐
		Set of 5 Gutter Pairs	7·00		☐	

968 Armagh Observatory, Jodrell Bank Radio Telescope and La Palma Telescope

969 Newton's Moon and Tides Diagram with Early Telescopes

970 Greenwich Old Observatory and Early Astronomical Equipment

971 Stonehenge, Gyroscope and Navigating by Stars

Astronomy

1990 (16 OCT.) *Phosphorised paper. Perf* $14 \times 14\frac{1}{2}$

1522	**968**	22p multicoloured	50	40	☐	☐
1523	**969**	26p multicoloured	80	90	☐	☐
1524	**970**	31p multicoloured	1·00	1·00	☐	☐
1525	**971**	37p multicoloured	1·10	1·10	☐	☐
		Set of 4	3·00	3·00	☐	☐
		First Day Cover		4·25		☐
		Presentation Pack	4·00		☐	
		PHQ Cards (set of 4)	2·50	5·50	☐	☐
		Set of 4 Gutter Pairs	6·00		☐	

Nos. 1522/5 commemorate the centenary of the British Astronomical Association and the bicentenary of the Armagh Observatory.

972 Building a Snowman

973 Fetching the Christmas Tree

974 Carol Singing

975 Tobogganing

976 Ice-skating

Christmas

1990 (13 Nov.) *One phosphor band (17p) or phosphorised paper (others)*

1526	**972**	17p multicoloured	45	35	☐	☐
1527	**973**	22p multicoloured	55	65	☐	☐
1528	**974**	26p multicoloured	80	80	☐	☐
1529	**975**	31p multicoloured	1·00	1·00	☐	☐
1530	**976**	37p multicoloured	1·10	1·10	☐	☐
		Set of 5	3·50	3·50	☐	☐
		First Day Cover		4·50		☐
		Presentation Pack	4·25		☐	
		PHQ Cards (set of 5)	3·25	6·00	☐	☐
		Set of 5 Gutter Pairs	7·00		☐	

Collectors Pack 1990

1990 (13 Nov.) *Comprises Nos. 1479/82, 1493/1510 and 1517/30*

	Collectors Pack	45·00	☐

Post Office Yearbook

1990 *Comprises Nos. 1479/82, 1493/500, 1502/10 and 1517/30 in hardback book with slip case.*

	Yearbook	50·00	☐

977 "King Charles Spaniel"

978 "A Pointer"

979 "Two Hounds in a Landscape"

981 "Fino and Tiny"

980 "A Rough Dog"

Dogs. Paintings by George Stubbs

1991 (8 Jan.) *Phosphorised paper. Perf* 14 × 14½

1531	**977**	22p multicoloured	..	75	75	☐ ☐
1532	**978**	26p multicoloured	..	90	80	☐ ☐
1533	**979**	31p multicoloured	..	1·00	85	☐ ☐
1534	**980**	33p multicoloured	..	1·10	95	☐ ☐
1535	**981**	37p multicoloured	..	1·25	1·10	☐ ☐
		Set of 5	.. .. ..	4·50	4·00	☐ ☐
		First Day Cover	.. ..		4·25	☐
		Presentation Pack	..	5·00		☐
		PHQ Cards (set of 5)	..	3·25	6·00	☐ ☐
		Set of 5 Gutter Pairs	..	9·00		☐

982 Thrush's Nest

983 Shooting Star and Rainbow

984 Magpies and Charm Bracelet

985 Black Cat

986 Common Kingfisher with Key

987 Mallard and Frog

988 Four-leaf Clover in Boot and Match Box

989 Pot of Gold at End of Rainbow

990 Heart-shaped Butterflies

991 Wishing Well and Sixpence

T **982/91** were printed together, *se-tenant*, in booklet panes of 10 stamps and 12 half stamp-size labels, the backgrounds of the stamps forming a composite design.

Greetings Booklet Stamps. "Good Luck"

1991 (5 Feb.) *Two phosphor bands.*

1536	**982**	(1st) multicoloured	..	1·40	1·40	☐ ☐
		a. Booklet pane. Nos.				
		1536/45	.. ..	12·50		☐
1537	**983**	(1st) multicoloured	..	1·40	1·40	☐ ☐
1538	**984**	(1st) multicoloured	..	1·40	1·40	☐ ☐
1539	**985**	(1st) multicoloured	..	1·40	1·40	☐ ☐
1540	**986**	(1st) multicoloured	..	1·40	1·40	☐ ☐
1541	**987**	(1st) multicoloured	..	1·40	1·40	☐ ☐
1542	**988**	(1st) multicoloured	..	1·40	1·40	☐ ☐
1543	**989**	(1st) multicoloured	..	1·40	1·40	☐ ☐
1544	**990**	(1st) multicoloured	..	1·40	1·40	☐ ☐
1545	**991**	(1st) multicoloured	..	1·40	1·40	☐ ☐
		Set of 10	.. .. ..	12·50	12·50	☐ ☐
		First Day Cover	.. .. ..		13·00	☐

992 Michael Faraday (inventor of electric motor) (Birth Bicentenary)

993 Charles Babbage (computer science pioneer) (Birth Bicentenary)

994 Radar Sweep of East Anglia (50th Anniv of Discovery by Sir Robert Watson-Watt)

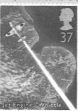

995 Gloster Whittle E28/39 Aircraft over East Anglia (50th Anniv of First Flight of Sir Frank Whittle's Jet Engine)

Scientific Achievements

1991 (5 Mar.) *Phosphorised paper*

1546	**992**	22p multicoloured	65	65	□ □
1547	**993**	22p multicoloured	65	65	□ □
1548	**994**	31p multicoloured	95	95	□ □
1549	**995**	37p multicoloured	1·10	1·10	□ □
	Set of 4		3·00	3·00	□ □
	First Day Cover			4·00	□
	Presentation Pack		3·75		□
	PHQ Cards (set of 4)		3·00	5·50	□ □
	Set of 4 Gutter Pairs		6·00		□

996 Teddy Bear

Nos. 1550/9 were printed together, *se-tenant*, in booklet panes of 10 stamps and 12 half stamp-size labels.

1991 (26 Mar.) *As Nos. 1483/92, but inscribed "1st" as T* **996**. *Two phosphor bands.*

1550	**996**	(1st) multicoloured	90	90	□ □
		a. Booklet pane. Nos. 1550/9	8·00		□
1551	**938**	(1st) multicoloured	90	90	□ □
1552	**939**	(1st) multicoloured	90	90	□ □
1553	**940**	(1st) multicoloured	90	90	□ □
1554	**941**	(1st) multicoloured	90	90	□ □
1555	**942**	(1st) multicoloured	90	90	□ □
1556	**943**	(1st) multicoloured	90	90	□ □
1557	**944**	(1st) multicoloured	90	90	□ □
1558	**945**	(1st) multicoloured	90	90	□ □
1559	**946**	(1st) multicoloured	90	90	□ □
	Set of 10		8·00	8·00	□ □
	First Day Cover			9·00	□

997 Man looking at Space

998

999 Space looking at Man   **1000**

Nos. 1560/1 and 1562/3 were each printed together, *se-tenant*, in horizontal pairs throughout the sheets, each pair forming a composite design.

Europa. Europe in Space

1991 (23 Apr.) *Phosphorised paper.*

1560	**997**	22p multicoloured	55	55	□ □
		a. Horiz pair. Nos. 1560/1	1·10	1·10	□ □
1561	**998**	22p multicoloured	55	55	□ □
1562	**999**	37p multicoloured	1·10	1·10	□ □
		a. Horiz pair. Nos. 1562/3	2·25	2·25	□ □
1563	**1000**	37p multicoloured	1·10	1·10	□ □
	Set of 4		3·00	3·00	□ □
	First Day Cover			4·00	□
	Presentation Pack		4·00		□
	PHQ Cards (set of 4)		3·00	5·50	□ □
	Set of 2 Gutter Strips of 4		6·00		□

1001 Fencing

1002 Hurdling

1003 Diving

1004 Rugby

World Student Games, Sheffield (Nos. 1564/6) and World Cup Rugby Championship, London (No. 1567)

1991 (11 JUNE) *Phosphorised paper. Perf* $14\frac{1}{2}$ × 14

1564	**1001**	22p multicoloured			50	50	☐	☐
1565	**1002**	26p multicoloured			80	80	☐	☐
1566	**1003**	31p multicoloured			95	95	☐	☐
1567	**1004**	37p multicoloured			1·10	1·10	☐	☐
	Set of 4				3·00	3·00	☐	☐
	First Day Cover					4·00		☐
	Presentation Pack			4·00			☐	
	PHQ Cards (set of 4)			3·00		5·50	☐	☐
	Set of 4 Gutter Pairs			6·00			☐	

1005 "Silver Jubilee"

1006 "Mme Alfred Carrière"

1007 *Rosa moyesii*

1008 "Harvest Fayre"

1009 "Mutabilis"

9th World Congress of Roses, Belfast

1991 (16 JULY) *Phosphorised paper. Perf* $14\frac{1}{2}$ × 14

1568	**1005**	22p multicoloured		75	50	☐	☐
1569	**1006**	26p multicoloured		90	80	☐	☐
1570	**1007**	31p multicoloured		1·00	85	☐	☐
1571	**1008**	33p multicoloured		1·10	95	☐	☐
1572	**1009**	37p multicoloured		1·25	1·25	☐	☐
	Set of 5			4·50	4·00	☐	☐
	First Day Cover				4·50		☐
	Presentation Pack		4·50			☐	
	PHQ Cards (set of 5)		3·25		7·00	☐	☐
	Set of 5 Gutter Pairs		9·00			☐	

1010 Iguanodon

1011 Stegosaurus

1012 Tyrannosaurus

1013 Protoceratops

1014 Triceratops

150th Anniversary of Dinosaurs' Identification by Owen

1991 (20 Aug.) *Phosphorised paper. Perf* $14\frac{1}{2} \times 14$

1573	**1010**	22p multicoloured		75	50	☐	☐
1574	**1011**	26p multicoloured		90	1·00	☐	☐
1575	**1012**	31p multicoloured		1·10	1·10	☐	☐
1576	**1013**	33p multicoloured		1·40	1·10	☐	☐
1577	**1014**	37p multicoloured		1·50	1·25	☐	☐
		Set of 5		5·00	4·50	☐	☐
		First Day Cover			5·00		☐
		Presentation Pack		5·50		☐	
		PHQ Cards (set of 5)		3·25	6·00	☐	☐
		Set of 5 Gutter Pairs		10·00		☐	

1015 Map of 1816

1016 Map of 1906

1017 Map of 1959

1018 Map of 1991

Bicentenary of Ordnance Survey. Maps of Hamstreet, Kent

1991 (17 Sept.) *Phosphorised paper. Perf* $14\frac{1}{2} \times 14$

1578	**1015**	24p multicoloured		50	50	☐	☐
1579	**1016**	28p multicoloured		80	85	☐	☐
1580	**1017**	33p multicoloured		95	1·00	☐	☐
1581	**1018**	39p multicoloured		1·10	1·25	☐	☐
		Set of 4		3·00	3·25	☐	☐
		First Day Cover			4·25		☐
		Presentation Pack		4·00		☐	
		PHQ Cards (set of 4)		3·00	6·00	☐	☐
		Set of 4 Gutter Pairs		6·00		☐	

1019 Adoration of the Magi

1020 Mary and Baby Jesus in Stable

1021 The Holy Family and Angel

1022 The Annunciation

1023 The Flight into Egypt

Christmas. Illuminated Manuscripts from the Bodleian Library, Oxford

1991 (12 Nov.) *One phosphor band (18p) or phosphorised paper (others)*

1582	**1019**	18p multicoloured		70	40	☐	☐
1583	**1020**	24p multicoloured		80	50	☐	☐
1584	**1021**	28p multicoloured		85	1·00	☐	☐
1585	**1022**	33p multicoloured		95	1·10	☐	☐
1586	**1023**	39p multicoloured		1·10	1·40	☐	☐
		Set of 5		4·00	4·00	☐	☐
		First Day Cover			4·50		☐
		Presentation Pack		4·25		☐	
		PHQ Cards (set of 5)		3·00	6·00	☐	☐
		Set of 5 Gutter Pairs		8·00		☐	

Collectors Pack 1991

1991 (12 Nov.) *Comprises Nos.* 1531/5, 1546/9 *and* 1560/86

	Collectors Pack	45·00	☐

Post Office Yearbook

1991 *Comprises Nos.* 1531/5, 1546/9 *and* 1560/86. *in hardback book with slip case.*

	Yearbook	50·00	☐

1024 Fallow Deer in Scottish Forest

1025 Hare on North Yorkshire Moors

1026 Fox in the Fens

1027 Redwing and Home Counties Village

1028 Welsh Mountain Sheep in Snowdonia

The Four Seasons. Wintertime

1992 (14 JAN.) *One phosphor band* (18p) *or phosphorised paper* (*others*)

1587	**1024**	18p multicoloured	..	45	50	☐ ☐
1588	**1025**	24p multicoloured	..	60	65	☐ ☐
1589	**1026**	28p multicoloured	..	80	75	☐ ☐
1590	**1027**	33p multicoloured	..	95	90	☐ ☐
1591	**1028**	39p multicoloured	..	1·10	1·10	☐ ☐
		Set of 5		3·50	3·50	☐ ☐
		First Day Cover			3·75	☐
		Presentation Pack		4·25		☐
		PHQ Cards (*set of 5*)..		3·00	7·00	☐ ☐
		Set of 5 Gutter Pairs ..		7·00		☐

1029 Flower Spray

1030 Double Locket

1031 Key

1032 Model Car and Cigarette Cards

1033 Compass and Map

1034 Pocket Watch

1035 1854 1d. Red Stamp and Pen

1036 Pearl Necklace

1037 Marbles

1038 Bucket, Spade and Starfish

T **1029**/38 were printed together, *se-tenant,* in booklet panes of 10 stamps and 12 half stamp-size labels, the backgrounds of the stamps forming a composite design.

Greetings Stamps. "Memories".

1992 (28 JAN.) *Two phosphor bands*

1592	**1029**	(1st) multicoloured	..	80	80	☐ ☐
		a. Booklet pane. Nos.				
		1592/1601	.. ..	7·00		☐
1593	**1030**	(1st) multicoloured	..	80	80	☐ ☐
1594	**1031**	(1st) multicoloured	..	80	80	☐ ☐
1595	**1032**	(1st) multicoloured	..	80	80	☐ ☐
1596	**1033**	(1st) multicoloured	..	80	80	☐ ☐
1597	**1034**	(1st) multicoloured	..	80	80	☐ ☐
1598	**1035**	(1st) multicoloured	..	80	80	☐ ☐
1599	**1036**	(1st) multicoloured	..	80	80	☐ ☐
1600	**1037**	(1st) multicoloured	..	80	80	☐ ☐
1601	**1038**	(1st) multicoloured	..	80	80	☐ ☐
		Set of 10		7·00	7·00	☐ ☐
		Presentation Pack		8·00		☐
		First Day Cover			8·50	☐

1039 Queen Elizabeth in Coronation Robes and Parliamentary Emblem

1040 Queen Elizabeth in Garter Robes and Archiepiscopal Arms

1041 Queen Elizabeth with Baby Prince Andrew and Royal Arms

1042 Queen Elizabeth at Trooping the Colour and Service Emblems

1043 Queen Elizabeth and Commonwealth Emblem

Nos. 1602-6 were printed together, *se-tenant*, in horizontal strips of 5 throughout the sheet, forming a composite design

40th Anniversary of Accession

1992 (6 Feb) *Two phosphor bands. Perf 14½ × 14.*

1602	**1039**	24p multicoloured	1·40	1·40	☐	☐
		a. Horiz strip of 5.				
		Nos. 1602/6	6·00	6·00	☐	☐
1603	**1040**	24p multicoloured	1·40	1·40	☐	☐
1604	**1041**	24p multicoloured	1·40	1·40	☐	☐
1605	**1042**	24p multicoloured	1·40	1·40	☐	☐
1606	**1043**	24p multicoloured	1·40	1·40	☐	☐
		Set of 5	6·00	6·00		
		First Day Cover		6·50	☐	
		Presentation Pack	6·50		☐	
		PHQ Cards (set of 5)	3·50	7·00	☐	
		Gutter Block of 10	12·00		☐	

1044 Tennyson in 1888 and "The Beguiling of Merlin" (Sir Edward Burne-Jones)

1045 Tennyson in 1856 and "April Love" (Arthur Hughes)

1046 Tennyson in 1864 and "I am Sick of the Shadows" (John Waterhouse)

1047 Tennyson as a Young Man and "Mariana" (Dante Gabriel Rossetti)

Death Centenary of Alfred, Lord Tennyson (poet)

1992 (10 Mar) *Phosphorised paper. Perf 14½ × 14*

1607	**1044**	24p multicoloured	50	50	☐	☐
1608	**1045**	28p multicoloured	65	65	☐	☐
1609	**1046**	33p multicoloured	1·10	1·10	☐	☐
1610	**1047**	39p multicoloured	1·10	1·10	☐	☐
		Set of 4	3·00	3·00	☐	☐
		First Day Cover		3·50	☐	
		Presentation Pack	3·75		☐	
		PHQ Cards (set of 4)	2·50	5·00	☐	☐
		Set of 4 Gutter Pairs	6·00		☐	

£1 CARRICKFERGUS CASTLE

1048 Carrickfergus Castle

1992 (24 Mar.)-**95**. *Designs as Nos. 1410/13, but showing Queen's head in silhouette as T 1048. Perf 15 × 14 (with one elliptical hole on each vertical side)*

1611	**1048**	£1 bottle green and gold†	5·00	1·50	☐	☐
1612	**882**	£1·50 maroon and gold†	2·25	2·25		☐
1613	**883**	£2 indigo and gold†	3·00	3·00	☐	☐
1613a	**1048**	£3 reddish violet and gold†	4·50	4·50	☐	☐
1614	**884**	£5 deep brown and gold†	7·50	7·50	☐	☐
		Set of 5	20·00	18·00		
		First Day Cover (Nos 1611, 1612, 1613, 1614)		30·00		☐
		First Day Cover (22 Aug 1995). (No. 1613a)		7·00		☐
		Presentation Pack (Nos. 1611/13, 1614)	16·00		☐	
		Presentation Pack (No. 1613a)	5·00		☐	
		PHQ Cards (Nos. 1611/14)	1·40		☐	
		PHQ Card (No. 1613a)	40	7·50	☐	☐
		Set of 5 Gutter Pairs	40·00		☐	

†The Queen's head on these stamps is printed in optically variable ink which changes colour from gold to green when viewed from different angles.

PHQ cards for Nos. 1611/13 and 1614 were not issued until 2 March 1993.

Nos. 1611/14 are printed by Harrison. For stamps with different lettering by Enschedé see Nos. 1993/6.

1049 British Olympic Association Logo (Olympic Games, Barcelona)

1050 British Paralympic Association Symbol (Paralympics '92, Barcelona)

1051 *Santa Maria* (500th Anniv of Discovery of America by Columbus)

1052 *Kaisei* (Japanese cadet brigantine) (Grand Regatta Columbus, 1992)

1053 British Pavilion, "EXPO '92", Seville

Nos. 1615/16 were printed together, *se-tenant*, in horizontal pairs throughout the sheet.

Europa. International Events

1992 (7 APR.) *Phosphorised paper. Perf* 14 × 14½

1615	**1049**	24p multicoloured	65	65	☐	☐
		a. Horiz pair.				
		Nos. 1615/16	1·25	1·25	☐	☐
1616	**1050**	24p multicoloured	65	65	☐	☐
1617	**1051**	24p multicoloured	65	65	☐	☐
1618	**1052**	39p multicoloured	1·10	1·10	☐	☐
1619	**1053**	39p multicoloured	1·10	1·10	☐	☐
		Set of 5	3·75	3·75	☐	☐
		First Day Cover		4·50		☐
		Presentation Pack	4·25		☐	
		PHQ Cards (set of 5)	3·00	6·00	☐	☐
		Set of 3 Gutter Pairs and a Gutter Strip of 4	7·50		☐	

1054 Pikeman

1055 Drummer

1056 Musketeer

1057 Standard Bearer

350th Anniversary of the Civil War

1992 (16 JUNE) *Phosphorised paper. Perf* 14½ × 14

1620	**1054**	24p multicoloured	55	55	☐	☐
1621	**1055**	28p multicoloured	70	70	☐	☐
1622	**1056**	33p multicoloured	1·00	1·00	☐	☐
1623	**1057**	39p multicoloured	1·10	1·10	☐	☐
		Set of 4	3·00	3·00	☐	☐
		First Day Cover		4·00		☐
		Presentation Pack	3·75		☐	
		PHQ Cards (set of 4)	2·00	5·00	☐	☐
		Set of 4 Gutter Pairs	6·00			

1058 *The Yeomen of the Guard*

1059 *The Gondoliers*

1060 *The Mikado*

1061 *The Pirates of Penzance*

1062 *Iolanthe*

150th Birth Anniversary of Sir Arthur Sullivan (composer). Gilbert and Sullivan Operas

1992 (21 JULY) *One phosphor band (18p) or phosphorised paper (others) Perf 14½ × 14*

1624	**1058**	18p multicoloured	..	40	45	□ □
1625	**1059**	24p multicoloured	..	55	55	□ □
1626	**1060**	28p multicoloured	..	70	70	□ □
1627	**1061**	33p multicoloured	..	1·10	1·10	□ □
1628	**1062**	39p multicoloured	..	1·25	1·25	□ □
		Set of 5		3·50	3·50	□ □
		First Day Cover	..		4·75	□
		Presentation Pack		4·00		□
		PHQ Cards (set of 5)	..	2·25	6·00	□ □
		Set of 5 Gutter Pairs	..	7·00		□

1063 "Acid Rain Kills"

1064 "Ozone Layer"

1065 "Greenhouse Effect"

1066 "Bird of Hope"

Protection of the Environment. Children's Paintings

1992 (15 SEPT) *Phosphorised paper. Perf 14 × 14½*

1629	**1063**	24p multicoloured	..	60	45	□ □
1630	**1064**	28p multicoloured	..	85	90	□ □
1631	**1065**	33p multicoloured	..	90	1·00	□ □
1632	**1066**	39p multicoloured	..	1·00	1·00	□ □
		Set of 4	..	3·00	3·00	□ □
		First Day Cover	..		3·75	□
		Presentation Pack		3·50		□
		PHQ Cards (set of 4)	..	2·00	5·50	□ □
		Set of 4 Gutter Pairs	..	6·00		□

1067 European Star

Single European Market

1992 (13 OCT) *Phosphorised paper*

1633	**1067**	24p multicoloured		75	75	□ □
		First Day Cover	..		1·50	□
		Presentation Pack		1·40		□
		PHQ Card	..	60	1·60	□ □
		Gutter Pair	..	1·50		□

1068 "Angel Gabriel", St. James's, Pangbourne

1069 "Madonna and Child", St. Mary's, Bibury

1070 "King with Gold", Our Lady and St. Peter, Leatherhead

1071 "Shepherds", All Saints, Porthcawl

1072 "Kings with Frankincense and Myrrh", Our Lady and St. Peter, Leatherhead

Christmas. Stained Glass Windows

1992 (10 Nov.) *One phosphor band (18p) or phosphorised paper (others).*

1634	**1068**	18p multicoloured	..	40	40	□ □
1635	**1069**	24p multicoloured	..	65	65	□ □
1636	**1070**	28p multicoloured	..	80	80	□ □
1637	**1071**	33p multicoloured	..	95	95	□ □
1638	**1072**	39p multicoloured	..	1·10	1·10	□ □
		Set of 5	..	3·50	3·50	□ □
		First Day Cover	..		4·25	□
		Presentation Pack		4·00		□
		PHQ Cards (set of 5)	..	2·25	5·50	□ □
		Set of 5 Gutter Pairs	..	7·00		□

Collectors Pack 1992

1992 (10 Nov.) *Comprises Nos. 1587/91, 1602/10 and 1615/38*

Collectors Pack .. .. .. 40·00 ☐

Post Office Yearbook

1992 (11 Nov.) *Comprises Nos. 1587/91, 1602/10 and 1615/38 in hardback book with slip case.*

Yearbook .. .. .. 45·00 ☐

600th Anniversary of Abbotsbury Swannery

1993 (19 Jan.) *One phosphor band (18p) or phosphorised paper (others)*

1639	**1073**	18p multicoloured	..	1·50	60	☐	☐
1640	**1074**	24p multicoloured	..	1·00	1·00	☐	☐
1641	**1075**	28p multicoloured	..	1·25	1·40	☐	☐
1642	**1076**	33p multicoloured	..	1·50	1·75	☐	☐
1643	**1077**	39p multicoloured	..	2·00	2·00	☐	☐
		Set of 5	..	6·50	6·00	☐	☐
		First Day Cover			6·50		☐
		Presentation Pack ..	..	7·00		☐	
		PHQ Cards (set of 5) ..	..	2·25	7·00	☐	☐
		Set of 5 Gutter Pairs ..	..	13·00		☐	

1073 Mute Swan Cob and St. Catherine's, Abbotsbury

1074 Cygnet and Decoy

1075 Swans and Cygnet

1076 Eggs in Nest and Tithe Barn, Abbotsbury

1077 Young Swan and the Fleet

1078 Long John Silver and Parrot (*Treasure Island*)

1079 Tweedledum and Tweedledee (*Alice Through the Looking-Glass*)

1080 William (*William* books)

1081 Mole and Toad (*The Wind in the Willows*)

1082 Teacher and Wilfrid ("The Bash Street Kids")

1083 Peter Rabbit and Mrs Rabbit (*The Tale of Peter Rabbit*)

1084 Snowman (*The Snowman*) and Father Christmas (*Father Christmas*)

1085 The Big Friendly Giant and Sophie (*The BFG*)

1086 Bill Badger and Rupert Bear

1087 Aladdin and the Genie

T 1078/87 were printed together, *se-tenant*, in booklet panes of 10 stamps and 20 half stamp-size labels.

Greetings Stamps. "Gift Giving"

1993 (2 FEB.) *Two phosphor bands. Perf* 15 × 14 (*with one elliptical hole on each vertical side*)

1644	**1078**	(1st) multicoloured	..	85	85	□	□
		a. Booklet pane. Nos.					
		1644/53	.. ..	7·50		□	
1645	**1079**	(1st) gold, cream and					
		black	.. ..	85	85	□	□
1646	**1080**	(1st) multicoloured	..	85	85	□	□
1647	**1081**	(1st) multicoloured	..	85	85	□	□
1648	**1082**	(1st) multicoloured	..	85	85	□	□
1649	**1083**	(1st) multicoloured	..	85	85	□	□
1650	**1084**	(1st) multicoloured	..	85	85	□	□
1651	**1085**	(1st) multicoloured	..	85	85	□	□
1652	**1086**	(1st) multicoloured	..	85	85	□	□
1653	**1087**	(1st) multicoloured	..	85	85	□	□
		Set of 10	..	7·50	7·50	□	□
		First Day Cover			8·00		□
		Presentation Pack		8·00		□	
		PHQ Cards (set of 10)		3·00	8·50	□	□

1088 Decorated Enamel Dial

1089 Escapement, Remontoire and Fusee

1090 Balance, Spring and Temperature Compensator

1091 Back of Movement

300th Birth Anniversary of John Harrison (inventor of the marine chronometer). Details of "H4" Clock

1993 (16 FEB.) *Phosphorised paper. Perf* 14½ × 14

1654	**1088**	24p multicoloured	..	50	50	□	□
1655	**1089**	28p multicoloured	..	80	80	□	□
1656	**1090**	33p multicoloured	..	95	95	□	□
1657	**1091**	39p multicoloured	..	1·10	1·10	□	□
		Set of 4		3·00	3·00	□	□
		First Day Cover			4·00		□
		Presentation Pack		4·00		□	
		PHQ Cards (set of 4) ..		2·00	4·50	□	□
		Set of 4 Gutter Pairs ..		6·00		□	

1092 Britannia

1993 (2 MAR.) *Granite paper. Perf* 14 × 14½ (*with two elliptical holes on each horizontal side*)

1658	**1092**	£10 multicoloured	..	15·00	6·00	□	□
		First Day Cover			25·00		□
		Presentation Pack		15·00		□	
		PHQ Card		35	25·00	□	□

1093 Dendrobium hellwigianum

1094 Paphiopedilum Maudiae "Magnificum"

1095 Cymbidium lowianum

1096 Vanda Rothschildiana

39 **1097** *Dendrobium vexillarius*
var. albiviride

14th World Orchid Conference, Glasgow

1993 (16 Mar.) *One phosphor band* (18p) *or phosphorised paper* (others).

1659	**1093**	18p multicoloured	..	40	40	☐ ☐
1660	**1094**	24p multicoloured	..	65	65	☐ ☐
1661	**1095**	28p multicoloured	..	90	90	☐ ☐
1662	**1096**	33p multicoloured	..	1·10	1·00	☐ ☐
1663	**1097**	39p multicoloured	..	1·40	1·25	☐ ☐
		Set of 5	.. .. ..	4·00	3·50	☐
		First Day Cover	.. ..		4·50	☐
		Presentation Pack	..	4·50		☐
		PHQ Cards (set of 5)	..	2·25	5·00	☐
		Set of 5 Gutter Pairs	..	8·00		☐

Booklet Stamps

1993 (6 Apr.)–**95** *As T* **916/17**, *but perf* 15 × 14 (*with one
elliptical hole on each vertical side*)

(a) Photo Harrison or Walsall (2nd) *or Harrison* (1st) *(both)*

1663a	**916**	(2nd)	bright blue (centre band)	30	35 ☐ ☐
1664	**917**	(1st)	bright orange-red (phosphorised paper)	60	55 ☐ ☐
1664a		(1st)	bright orange-red (2 phosphor bands)	40	45 ☐ ☐

(b) Litho Questa or Walsall (*No.*1666 *also Enschedé*)

1665	**916**	(2nd)	bright blue (1 centre band)	30	35 ☐ ☐
1666	**917**	(1st)	bright orange-red (2 phosphor bands)	40	45 ☐ ☐

Nos. 1663a and 1665/6 also come from sheets.
For 1st in gold see No. 1979.

1993-97 *As Nos.* X841, *etc, but perf* 15 × 14 (*with one
elliptical hole on each vertical side*)

(a) Photo Harrison (19p, 20p (Nos. Y1675/b), 25p (*No.*
Y1676), 26p, 35p (*No.* Y1683), 41p (*No.* Y1689), 43p
(*No.* Y1691), *Enschedé* (20p (*No.* Y1674), 29p, 35p (*No.*
Y1682), 36p, 38p, 41p (*No.* Y1688), 43p (*No.* Y1690),
Harrison, Enschedé or Walsall (37p, 63p), *Harrison or
Enschedé* (*others*)

Y1667	**369**	1p crimson (2 bands) ..	10	10 ☐ ☐
Y1668		2p deep green (2 bands)	10	10 ☐ ☐
Y1669		4p new blue (2 bands)	10	10 ☐ ☐
Y1670		5p dull red-brown (2 bands)	10	10 ☐ ☐
Y1671		6p yellow-olive (2 bands)	10	15 ☐ ☐
Y1672		10p dull orange (2 bands)	15	20 ☐ ☐
Y1673		19p bistre (1 centre band)	30	35 ☐ ☐
Y1674		20p turquoise-green (2 bands)	50	50 ☐ ☐
Y1675		20p bright green (1 centre band)	30	35 ☐ ☐
Y1675b		20p bright green (1 side band)	1·00	1·00 ☐ ☐
Y1676		25p rose-red (phos- phorised paper)	70	70 ☐ ☐
Y1677		25p rose-red (2 bands)	60	60 ☐ ☐
Y1678		26p red-brown (2 bands)	40	45 ☐ ☐
Y1679		29p grey (2 bands) ..	70	70 ☐ ☐
Y1680		30p deep olive-grey (2 bands)	45	50 ☐ ☐
Y1681		31p deep mauve (2 bands)	50	55 ☐ ☐
Y1682		35p yellow (2 bands) ..	85	85 ☐ ☐
Y1683		35p yellow (phosphor- ised paper)	85	85 ☐ ☐
Y1684		36p bright ultramarine..	85	85 ☐ ☐
Y1685		37p bright mauve (2 bands)	60	65 ☐ ☐
Y1686		38p rosine (2 bands) ..	90	90 ☐ ☐
Y1687		39p bright magenta (2 bands)	60	65 ☐ ☐
Y1688		41p grey-brown (2 bands)	1·00	1·00 ☐ ☐
Y1689		41p drab (phosphorised paper)	1·00	1·00 ☐ ☐
Y1690		43p deep olive-brown (2 bands)	65	70 ☐ ☐
Y1691		43p sepia (2 bands) ..	65	70 ☐ ☐
Y1692		50p ochre (2 bands) ..	75	80 ☐ ☐
Y1693		63p light emerald (2 bands)	95	1·00 ☐ ☐
Y1694		£1 bluish violet (2 bands)	1·50	1·60 ☐ ☐

(b) Litho Walsall (37p, 60p, 63p), Questa or Walsall (25p, 35p, 41p), Questa (others)

Y1743	**369**	1p lake (2 bands)	10	10	☐	☐
Y1748		6p yellow-olive (2 bands)	3·75	3·75	☐	·
Y1749		10p dull orange (2 bands)	2·25	2·25	☐	☐
Y1750		19p bistre (1 side band)	1·00	1·00	☐	☐
Y1751		20p bright yellow-green (1 centre band) ..	30	35	☐	☐
Y1752		25p red (2 bands) ..	60	60	☐	☐
Y1753		26p chestnut (2 bands)	40	45	☐	☐
Y1754		30p olive-grey (2 bands)	2·25	2·25	☐	☐
Y1755		35p yellow (2 bands) ..	85	85	☐	☐
Y1756		37p bright mauve (2 bands)	60	65	☐	☐
Y1757		41p drab (2 bands) ..	1·00	1·00	☐	☐
Y1758		60p dull blue-grey (2 bands)	1·50	1·50	☐	☐
Y1759		63p light emerald (2 bands)	95	1·00	☐	☐
		First Day Cover (Nos. Y1673, Y1676, Y1679, Y1684, Y1686, Y1688) (26.10.93)		4·50	☐	
		First Day Cover (No. Y1758) (9.8.94)		2·00	☐	
		First Day Cover (No. Y1694) (22.8.95)		2·75	☐	
		First Day Cover (Nos. Y1675, Y1678, Y1681, Y1685, Y1687, Y1690, Y1693) (25.6.96)		5·50	☐	
		Presentation Pack (Nos. Y1673, Y1676, Y1679, Y1684, Y1686, Y1688) ..	5·00		☐	
		Presentation Pack (Nos. Y1667/74, Y1677, Y1679/80, Y1682, Y1684, Y1686, Y1688, Y1692, Y1694, Y1758)	12·00		☐	
		Presentation Pack (Nos. Y1675, Y1678, Y1681, Y1685, Y1687, Y1690, Y1693)	4·50		☐	
		PHQ Card (No. Y1694)	40	2·75	☐	☐

No. Y1694 is printed in Iriodin ink which gives a shiny effect to the solid part of the background behind the Queen's head.

Nos. Y1683 and Y1689 were only issued in coils and Nos. Y1675b, Y1748/50, Y1752, Y1754/5 and Y1757/8 only in booklets.

No. Y1750 exists with the phosphor band at the left or right of the stamp, but No. Y1675b exists with band at right only.

For 26p in gold see No. 1978.

1098 "Family Group"
(bronze sculpture)
(Henry Moore)

1099 "Kew Gardens"
(lithograph) (Edward
Bawden)

1100 "St. Francis and the
Birds" (Stanley
Spencer)

1101 "Still Life: Odyssey
I" (Ben Nicholson)

Europa. Contemporary Art

1993 (11 MAY) Phosphorised paper. Perf 14 x 14½

1767	**1098** 24p multicoloured	..	50	50	☐	☐
1768	**1099** 28p multicoloured	..	80	80	☐	☐
1769	**1100** 33p multicoloured	..	95	95	☐	☐
1770	**1101** 39p multicoloured	..	1·10	1·10	☐	☐
	Set of 4	..	3·00	3·00	☐	☐
	First Day Cover ..	.. ..		4·00		☐
	Presentation Pack	.. ..	3·50		☐	
	PHQ Cards (set of 4)	..	2·00	4·50	☐	☐
	Set of 4 Gutter Pairs	..	6·00		☐	

1102 Emperor Claudius
(from gold coin)

1103 Emperor Hadrian
(bronze head)

1104 Goddess Roma
(from gemstone)

1105 Christ (Hinton St
Mary mosaic)

Roman Britain

1993 (15 JUNE) Phosphorised paper with two phosphor
bands. Perf 14 x 14½

1771	**1102** 24p multicoloured	.. ..	50	50	☐	☐
1772	**1103** 28p multicoloured	.. ..	80	80	☐	☐
1773	**1104** 33p multicoloured	.. ..	95	95	☐	☐
1774	**1105** 39p multicoloured	.. ..	1·10	1·10	☐	☐
	Set of 4	..	3·00	3·00	☐	☐
	First Day Cover			4·00		☐
	Presentation Pack	.. ..	3·50		☐	
	PHQ Cards (set of 4)		1·40	4·00	☐	☐
	Set of 4 Gutter Pairs	..	6·00		☐	

1106 Midland Maid and
other Narrow Boats,
Grand Junction Canal

1107 Yorkshire Maid and
other Humber Keels,
Stainforth and Keadby
Canal

1108 Valley Princess and
other Horse-drawn
Barges, Brecknock and
Abergavenny Canal

1109 Steam Barges,
including Pride of
Scotland, and Fishing
Boats, Crinan Canal

Inland Waterways

1993 (20 JULY) Two phosphor bands. Perf 14½ x 14

1775	**1106** 24p multicoloured	..	50	50	☐	☐
1776	**1107** 28p multicoloured	..	80	80	☐	☐
1777	**1108** 33p multicoloured	..	95	95	☐	☐
1778	**1109** 39p multicoloured	..	1·10	1·10	☐	☐
	Set of 4		3·00	3·00	☐	☐
	First Day Cover ..	.. ..		4·00		☐
	Presentation Pack	.. ..	3·50		☐	
	PHQ Cards (set of 4)	..	1·40	4·50	☐	☐
	Set of 4 Gutter Pairs	..	6·00		☐	

Nos. 1775/8 commemorate the bicentenaries of the Acts
of Parliament authorising the canals depicted.

1110 Horse Chestnut

1111 Blackberry

1112 Hazel

1113 Rowan

1114 Pear

SHERLOCK HOLMES & MORIARTY
"THE FINAL PROBLEM"

1119 The Final Problem

T **1115/19** were printed together, *se-tenant*, in horizontal strips of 5 throughout the sheet.

The Four Seasons. Autumn. Fruits and Leaves

1993 (14 Sept.) One phosphor band (18p) or phosphorised paper (others)

1779	**1110**	18p multicoloured	..	40	40	☐	☐
1780	**1111**	24p multicoloured	..	65	65	☐	☐
1781	**1112**	28p multicoloured	..	90	80	☐	☐
1782	**1113**	33p multicoloured	..	1·10	95	☐	☐
1783	**1114**	39p multicoloured	..	1·40	1·10	☐	☐
		Set of 5	.. .. ..	4·00	3·50	☐	
		First Day Cover	.. ..		4·50	☐	
		Presentation Pack	.. ..	4·25		☐	
		PHQ Cards (set of 5)	.. ..	1·50	5·00	☐	☐
		Set of 5 Gutter Pairs	.. ..	8·00		☐	

Sherlock Holmes. Centenary of the Publication of The Final Problem

1993 (12 Oct.) Phosphorised paper. Perf 14 × 14½

1784	**1115**	24p multicoloured	..	90	90	☐	☐
		a. Horiz strip of 5.					
		Nos. 1784/8		4·00	4·00	☐	☐
1785	**1116**	24p multicoloured	..	90	90	☐	☐
1786	**1117**	24p multicoloured	..	90	90	☐	☐
1787	**1118**	24p multicoloured	..	90	90	☐	☐
1788	**1119**	24p multicoloured	..	90	90	☐	☐
		Set of 5	.. ..	4·00	4·00	☐	☐
		First Day Cover	.. ..		4·75		☐
		Presentation Pack	..	4·50		☐	
		PHQ Cards (set of 5)	..	1·50	5·50	☐	☐
		Gutter strip of 10	..	8·00		☐	

SHERLOCK HOLMES & DR WATSON
"THE REIGATE SQUIRE"

1115 The Reigate Squire

SHERLOCK HOLMES & SIR HENRY
"THE HOUND OF THE BASKERVILLES"

1116 The Hound of the Baskervilles

1120

Self-adhesive Booklet Stamp

1993 (19 Oct.) Litho Walsall. Two phosphor bands. Die-cut perf 14 × 15 (with one elliptical hole on each vertical side)

1789	**1120**	(1st) orange-red..	..	1·00	1·00	☐	☐
		First Day Cover	.. ..		3·25		☐
		Presentation Pack (booklet					
		pane of 20)	.. ..	12·00		☐	
		PHQ Card	.. ..	30	3·25	☐	☐

For similar 2nd and 1st designs printed in photogravure by Enschedé see Nos. 1976/7.

SHERLOCK HOLMES & LESTRADE
"THE SIX NAPOLEONS"

1117 The Six Napoleons

SHERLOCK HOLMES & MYCROFT
"THE GREEK INTERPRETER"

1118 The Greek Interpreter

1121 Bob Cratchit and Tiny Tim

1122 Mr and Mrs Fezziwig

1123 Scrooge

1124 The Prize Turkey

1128 Class "4" No. 43000 on Turntable at Blyth North

1129 Class "4" No. 42455 near Wigan Central

1125 Mr. Scrooge's Nephew

1130 Class "Castle" No. 7002 *Devizes Castle* on Bridge crossing Worcester and Birmingham Canal

Christmas. 150th Anniversary of Publication of A Christmas Carol

1993 (9 Nov.) *One phosphor band. (19p) or phosphorised paper (others)*

1790	**1121**	19p multicoloured	..	40	40	☐	☐
1791	**1122**	25p multicoloured	..	65	65	☐	☐
1792	**1123**	30p multicoloured	..	80	80	☐	☐
1793	**1124**	35p multicoloured	..	95	95	☐	☐
1794	**1125**	41p multicoloured	..	1·10	1·10	☐	☐
		Set of 5		3·50	3·50	☐	☐
		First Day Cover			4·50		☐
		Presentation Pack		4·00		☐	
		PHQ Cards (set of 5)		1·90	5·25	☐	☐
		Set of 5 Gutter Pairs		7·25		☐	

Collectors Pack 1993

1993 (9 Nov.) *Comprises Nos. 1639/43, 1654/7, 1659/63, 1767/88 and 1790/4*

Collectors Pack	40·00	☐

Post Office Yearbook

1993 (9 Nov.) *Comprises Nos. 1639/43, 1654/7, 1659/63, 1767/88 and 1790/4 in hardback book with slip case*

Yearbook	45·00	☐

The Age of Steam. Railway Photographs by Colin Gifford

1994 (18 Jan.) *One phosphor band (19p) or phosphorised paper with two bands (others). Perf 14½*

1795	**1126**	19p deep blue-green, grey-black and black	..	45	40	☐	☐
1796	**1127**	25p slate-lilac, grey-black and black	..	75	65	☐	☐
1797	**1128**	30p lake-brown, grey-black and black	..	90	80	☐	☐
1798	**1129**	35p deep claret, grey-black and black	..	1·10	95	☐	☐
1799	**1130**	41p indigo, grey-black and black ..	..	1·25	1·10	☐	☐
		Set of 5		4·00	3·50	☐	☐
		First Day Cover			4·50		☐
		Presentation Pack		4·25		☐	
		PHQ Cards (set of 5)		1·90	5·25	☐	☐
		Set of 5 Gutter Pairs		8·00		☐	

126 Class "5" No. 44957 and Class "B1" No. 61342 on West Highland Line

1127 Class "A1" No. 60149 *Amadis* at Kings Cross

1131 Dan Dare and the Mekon

1132 The Three Bears

1133 Rupert Bear

1134 Alice (*Alice in Wonderland*)

1135 Noggin and the Ice Dragon

1136 Peter Rabbit posting Letter

1137 Red Riding Hood and Wolf

1138 Orlando the Marmalade Cat

1139 Biggles

1140 Paddington Bear on Station

T **1131/40** were printed together, *se-tenant*, in booklet panes of 10 stamps and 20 half stamp-size labels.

Greetings Stamps. "Messages"

1994 (1 Feb.) Two phosphor bands. Perf 15 × 14 (*with one elliptical hole on each vertical side*)

1800 **1131**	(1st) multicoloured	..	40	45 ☐ ☐
	a. Booklet pane.			
	Nos. 1800/9 ..	..	4·00	☐
1801 **1132**	(1st) multicoloured	..	40	45 ☐ ☐
1802 **1133**	(1st) multicoloured	..	40	45 ☐ ☐
1803 **1134**	(1st) gold, bistre-yellow			
	and black	..	40	45 ☐ ☐
1804 **1135**	(1st) multicoloured	..	40	45 ☐ ☐
1805 **1136**	(1st) multicoloured	..	40	45 ☐ ☐

1806 **1137**	(1st) multicoloured	..	40	45 ☐ ☐
1807 **1138**	(1st) multicoloured	..	40	45 ☐ ☐
1808 **1139**	(1st) multicoloured	..	40	45 ☐ ☐
1809 **1140**	(1st) multicoloured	..	40	45 ☐ ☐
	Set of 10	..	4·00	4·50 ☐ ☐
	First Day Cover			7·50
	Presentation Pack	..	11·00	☐
	PHQ Cards (set of 10) ..	..	4·25	10·00 ☐

1141 Castell Y Waun (Chirk Castle), Clwyd, Wales

1142 Ben Arkle, Sutherland, Scotland

1143 Mourne Mountains, County Down, Northern Ireland

1144 Dersingham, Norfolk, England

1145 Dolwyddelan, Gwynedd, Wales

25th Anniversary of Investiture of the Prince Wales. Paintings by Prince Charles

1994 (1 Mar.) One phosphor band (19p) or phosphoris paper (*others*)

1810 **1141**	19p multicoloured ..	..	40	40 ☐
1811 **1142**	25p multicoloured ..	..	75	75 ☐
1812 **1143**	30p multicoloured ..	..	1·00	1·00 ☐
1813 **1144**	35p multicoloured ..	..	1·10	1·10 ☐
1814 **1145**	41p multicoloured ..	..	1·25	1·25 ☐
	Set of 5	..	4·00	4·00 ☐
	First Day Cover			4·50
	Presentation Pack	..	4·50	☐
	PHQ Cards (set of 5) ..	..	1·90	5·25 ☐
	Set of 5 Gutter Pairs ..	..	8·00	

146 Bather at
Blackpool

1147 "Where's my
Little Lad?"

148 "Wish You were
Here!"

1149 Punch and Judy
Show

1150 "The Tower Crane" Machine

1151 British Lion and French
Cockerel over Tunnel

1152 Symbolic Hands over
Train

Nos. 1820/1 and 1822/3 were printed together, *se-tenant,* in horizontal pairs throughout the sheets.

Opening of Channel Tunnel

1994 (3 May) *Phosphorised paper. Perf* $14 \times 14\frac{1}{2}$

1820	**1151**	25p multicoloured	..	60	60	☐	☐
		a. *Horiz pair. Nos.*					
		1820/1	.. ..	1·25	1·25	☐	☐
1821	**1152**	25p multicoloured	..	60	60	☐	☐
1822	**1151**	41p multicoloured	..	1·40	1·40	☐	☐
		a. *Horiz pair. Nos.*					
		1822/3	.. ..	2·75	2·75	☐	☐
1823	**1152**	41p multicoloured	..	1·40	1·40	☐	☐
		Set of 4 ..	.. ..	3·50	3·50	☐	☐
		First Day Cover	.. ..		5·00		☐
		Presentation Pack	.. ..	4·00		☐	
		PHQ Cards (set of 4)	.. ..	1·75	6·00	☐	☐

Stamps in similar designs were also issued by France.

Centenary of Picture Postcards

1994 (12 Apr.) *One side band (19p) or two phosphor bands (others). Perf* $14 \times 14\frac{1}{2}$

1815	**1146**	19p multicoloured	.. ..	40	40	☐	☐
1816	**1147**	25p multicoloured	.. ..	65	65	☐	☐
1817	**1148**	30p multicoloured	.. ..	80	80	☐	☐
1818	**1149**	35p multicoloured	.. ..	95	95	☐	☐
1819	**1150**	41p multicoloured	.. ..	1·10	1·10	☐	☐
		Set of 5	.. ..	3·50	3·50	☐	☐
		First Day Cover	.. ..		4·00		☐
		Presentation Pack	.. ..	4·00		☐	
		PHQ Cards (set of 5)	.. ..	1·90	5·25	☐	☐
		Set of 5 Gutter Pairs	.. ..	7·25		☐	

1153 Groundcrew
replacing Smoke
Canisters on Douglas
Boston of 88 Sqn

1154 H.M.S. *Warspite*
(battleship) shelling
Enemy Positions

1155 Commandos landing on Gold Beach

1156 Infantry regrouping on Sword Beach

1157 Tank and Infantry advancing, Ouistreham

Nos. 1824/8 were printed together, *se-tenant*, in horizontal strips of 5 throughout the sheet.

50th Anniversary of D-Day

1994 (6 JUNE) *Two phosphor bands. Perf* $14\frac{1}{2} \times 14$

1824	**1153** 25p multicoloured	..	..	80	80	☐	☐
	a. Horiz strip of 5.						
	Nos. 1824/8	..	..	3·50	3·50	☐	☐
1825	**1154** 25p multicoloured	..	..	80	80	☐	☐
1826	**1155** 25p multicoloured	..	..	80	80	☐	☐
1827	**1156** 25p multicoloured	..	..	80	80	☐	☐
1828	**1157** 25p multicoloured	..	..	80	80	☐	☐
	Set of 5	..	..	3·50	3·50	☐	☐
	First Day Cover	..	..		4·00		☐
	Presentation Pack	..	..	3·75		☐	
	PHQ Cards (set of 5)	..	..	2·00	5·00	☐	☐
	Gutter Block of 10	..	..	7·00		☐	

1158 The Old Course, St. Andrews

1159 The 18th Hole, Muirfield

1160 The 15th Hole ("Luckyslap"), Carnoustie

1161 The 8th Hole ("The Postage Stamp"), Royal Troon

1162 The 9th Hole, Turnberry

Scottish Golf Courses

1994 (5 JULY) *One phosphor band* (19p) *or phosphorised paper* (others). *Perf* $14\frac{1}{2} \times 14$

1829	**1158** 19p multicoloured	..	..	55	55	☐	☐
1830	**1159** 25p multicoloured	..	..	80	80	☐	☐
1831	**1160** 30p multicoloured	..	..	1·00	1·00	☐	☐
1832	**1161** 35p multicoloured	..	..	1·25	1·25	☐	☐
1833	**1162** 41p multicoloured	..	..	1·40	1·40	☐	☐
	Set of 5	..	..	4·50	4·50	☐	☐
	First Day Cover	..	..		4·75		☐
	Presentation Pack	..	..	4·75		☐	
	PHQ Cards (set of 5)	..	..	2·25	5·75	☐	☐
	Set of 5 Gutter Pairs	..	..	9·00		☐	

Nos. 1829/33 commemorate the 250th anniversary of golf's first set of rules produced by the Honourable Company of Edinburgh Golfers.

1163 Royal Welsh Show, Llanelwedd

1164 All England Tennis Championships, Wimbledon

1165 Cowes Week

1166 Test Match, Lord's

SUMMERTIME Braemar

1167 Braemar Gathering

The Four Seasons. Summertime. Events

1994 (2 Aug.) *One phosphor band* (19p) *or phosphorised paper* (*others*)

1834	**1163** 19p multicoloured	..	..	50	50	☐ ☐
1835	**1164** 25p multicoloured	..	..	70	70	☐ ☐
1836	**1165** 30p multicoloured	..	..	90	80	☐ ☐
1837	**1166** 35p multicoloured	..	..	1·00	90	☐ ☐
1838	**1167** 41p multicoloured	..	..	1·10	1·00	☐ ☐
	Set of 5	.. .. ..	..	3·75	3·50	☐
	First Day Cover ..	.. ..			4·25	☐
	Presentation Pack	.. ..	..	4·00		☐
	PHQ Cards (set of 5)	..	..	1·90	5·25	☐ ☐
	Set of 5 Gutter Pairs	..	..	7·50		☐

1168 Ultrasonic Imaging

1169 Scanning Electron Microscopy

1170 Magnetic Resonance Imaging

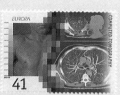

1171 Computed Tomography

Europa. Medical Discoveries

1994 (27 Sept.) *Phosphorised paper. Perf* $14 \times 14\frac{1}{2}$

1839	**1168** 25p multicoloured	..	..	65	65	☐ ☐
1840	**1169** 30p multicoloured	..	..	85	85	☐ ☐
1841	**1170** 35p multicoloured	..	..	90	90	☐ ☐
1842	**1171** 41p multicoloured	..	..	1·00	1·00	☐ ☐
	Set of 4	.. .. ..	..	3·00	3·00	☐ ☐
	First Day Cover ..	.. ..			4·00	☐
	Presentation Pack	.. ..		4·00		☐
	PHQ Cards (set of 4)	..	..	1·50	3·50	☐ ☐
	Set of 4 Gutter Pairs	..	..	6·00		☐

1172 Virgin Mary and Joseph

1173 Three Wise Men

1174 Virgin and Child

1175 Shepherds

1176 Angels

Christmas, Children's Nativity Plays

1994 (1 Nov.) *One phosphor band* (19p) *or phosphorised paper* (*others*)

1843	**1172** 19p multicoloured	..	..	50	50	☐ ☐
1844	**1173** 25p multicoloured	..	..	70	70	☐ ☐
1845	**1174** 30p multicoloured	..	..	80	80	☐ ☐
1846	**1175** 35p multicoloured	..	..	90	90	☐ ☐
1847	**1176** 41p multicoloured	..	..	1·00	1·00	☐ ☐
	Set of 5	.. .. ..	..	3·50	3·50	☐ ☐
	First Day Cover ..	.. ..			4·25	☐
	Presentation Pack	.. ..	..	4·00		☐
	PHQ Cards (set of 5)	..	..	1·90	5·25	☐ ☐
	Set of 5 Gutter Pairs	..	..	7·00		☐

Collectors Pack 1994

1994 (14 Nov.) *Comprises Nos.* 1795/1847.

	Collectors Pack	.. .. ..	40·00	☐

Post Office Yearbook

1994 (14 Nov.) *Comprises Nos.* 1795/9 *and* 1810/47 *in hardback book with slip case.*

	Yearbook	.. .. ..	45·00	☐

1177 Sophie (black cat)

1178 Puskas (Siamese) and Tigger (tabby)

1179 Chloe (ginger cat)

1180 Kikko (tortoiseshell) and Rosie (Abyssinian)

1181 Fred (black and white cat)

Cats

1995 (17 JAN.) *One phosphor band* (19p) *or two phosphor bands* (others). *Perf* $14\frac{1}{2} \times 14$

1848	**1177**	19p multicoloured	.. ..	60	60	☐ ☐
1849	**1178**	25p multicoloured	.. ..	75	75	☐ ☐
1850	**1179**	30p multicoloured	.. ..	1·00	1·10	☐ ☐
1851	**1180**	35p multicoloured	.. ..	1·10	1·10	☐ ☐
1852	**1181**	41p multicoloured	.. ..	1·25	1·25	☐ ☐
	Set of 5	..	.. .. ..	4·25	4·25	☐ ☐
	First Day Cover	..	.. ..		4·50	☐
	Presentation Pack	..	..	4·50		☐
	PHQ Cards (*set of 5*)		.. ..	2·50	6·00	☐ ☐
	Set of 5 Gutter Pairs		.. ..	8·50		☐

1182 Dandelions

1183 Sweet Chestnut Leaves

1184 Garlic Leaves

1185 Hazel Leaves

1186 Spring Grass

The Four Seasons. Springtime. Plant Sculptures by Andy Goldsworthy

1995 (14 MAR.) *One phosphor band* (19p) *or two phosphor bands* (others).

1853	**1182**	19p multicoloured	.. ..	55	55	☐ ☐
1854	**1183**	25p multicoloured	.. ..	65	65	☐ ☐
1855	**1184**	30p multicoloured	.. ..	90	90	☐ ☐
1856	**1185**	35p multicoloured	.. ..	1·00	1·00	☐ ☐
1857	**1186**	41p multicoloured	.. ..	1·10	1·10	☐ ☐
	Set of 5	..	.. ..	3·75	3·75	☐ ☐
	First Day Cover ..		.. ..		4·00	☐
	Presentation Pack	..	..	4·00		☐
	PHQ Cards (*set of 5*)		.. ..	2·25	5·25	☐ ☐
	Set of 5 Gutter Pairs		.. ..	7·50		☐

1187 "La Danse a la Campagne" (Renoir)

1188 "Troilus and Criseyde" (Peter Brookes)

1189 "The Kiss" (Rodin)

1190 "Girls on the Town" (Beryl Cook)

1191 "Jazz" (Andrew Mockett)

1192 "Girls performing a Kathal Dance" (Aurangzeb period)

1193 "Alice Keppel with her Daughter" (Alice Hughes)

1194 "Children Playing" (L. S. Lowry)

1195 "Circus Clowns" (Emily Firmin and Justin Mitchell)

1196 Decoration from "All the Love Poems of Shakespeare" (Eric Gill)

T 1187/96 were printed together, *se-tenant*, in booklet panes of 10 stamps and 20 half stamp-size labels.

Greetings Stamp. "Greetings in Art"

1995 (21 MAR.) *Two phosphor bands. Perf* $14\frac{1}{2} \times 14$ (*with one elliptical hole on each vertical side*)

1858	**1187**	(1st) multicoloured	..	40	45	□ □
		a. Booklet pane. Nos.				
		1858/67	.. ..	4·00		□
1859	**1188**	(1st) multicoloured	..	40	45	□ □
1860	**1189**	(1st) multicoloured	..	40	45	□ □
1861	**1190**	(1st) multicoloured	..	40	45	□ □
1862	**1191**	(1st) multicoloured	..	40	45	□ □
1863	**1192**	(1st) multicoloured	..	40	45	□ □
1864	**1193**	(1st) purple-brown and silver		40	45	□ □
1865	**1194**	(1st) multicoloured	..	40	45	□ □
1866	**1195**	(1st) multicoloured	..	40	45	□ □
1867	**1196**	(1st) black, greenish yellow & silver		40	45	□ □
		Set of 10	..	4·00	4·25	□ □
		First Day Cover	..		7·00	□
		Presentation Pack ..	..	4·25		□
		PHQ Cards (set of 10) ..	..	3·75	8·75	□

The National Trust *Celebrating 100 Years* **19**

1197 Fireplace Decoration, Attingham Park, Shropshire

The National Trust *Protecting Land* **25**

1198 Oak Seedling

The National Trust *Conserving Art* **30**

1199 Carved Table Leg, Attingham Park

The National Trust *Saving Coast* **35**

1200 St. David's Head, Dyfed, Wales

The National Trust *Repairing Buildings* **41**

1201 Elizabethan Window, Little Moreton Hall, Cheshire

Centenary of The National Trust

1995 (11 APR.) *One phosphor band* (19p), *two phosphor bands* (25p, 35p) *or phosphorised paper* (30p, 41p).

1868	**1197**	19p multicoloured ..	..	55	55	□ □
1869	**1198**	25p multicoloured ..	..	65	65	□ □
1870	**1199**	30p multicoloured ..	..	80	80	□ □
1871	**1200**	35p multicoloured ..	..	90	90	□ □
1872	**1201**	41p multicoloured ..	..	1·10	1·10	□ □
		Set of 5	..	3·50	3·50	□ □
		First Day Cover	..		3·75	□
		Presentation Pack ..	..	3·75		□
		PHQ Cards (set of 5) ..	..	1·90	5·25	□ □
		Set of 5 Gutter Pairs ..	..	7·00		□

1202 British Troops and French Civilians celebrating

1203 Symbolic Hands and Red Cross

1204 St. Paul's Cathedral and Searchlights

1205 Symbolic Hand releasing Peace Dove

1206 Symbolic Hands

Europa. Peace and Freedom

1995 (2 MAY) *One phosphor band* (*Nos.* 1873/4) *or two phosphor bands* (*others*). *Perf* $14\frac{1}{2} \times 14$

1873	**1202** 19p silver, bistre-brown and grey-black	..	50	50	☐	☐
1874	**1203** 19p multicoloured ..	..	50	50	☐	☐
1875	**1204** 25p silver, blue and grey-black	.. ..	65	65	☐	☐
1876	**1205** 25p multicoloured ..	..	65	65	☐	☐
1877	**1206** 30p multicoloured ..	..	75	75	☐	☐
	Set of 5		2·75	2·75	☐	☐
	First Day Cover			3·00		☐
	Presentation Pack		3·00		☐	
	PHQ Cards (set of 5)		1·90	4·50	☐	☐
	Set of 5 Gutter Pairs		5·50		☐	

Nos. 1873 and 1875 commemorate the 50th anniversary of the end of the Second World War, No. 1874 the 125th anniversary of the British Red Cross Society and Nos. 1876/7 the 50th anniversary of the United Nations.

Nos. 1876/7 include the "EUROPA" emblem.

1207 *The Time Machine*

1208 *The First Men in the Moon*

1209 *The War of the Worlds*

1210 *The Shape of Things to Come*

Science Fiction. Novels by H. G. Wells

1995 (6 JUNE) *Two phosphor bands. Perf* $14\frac{1}{2} \times 14$

1878	**1207**	25p multicoloured ..	..	65	65	☐	☐
1879	**1208**	30p multicoloured ..	..	85	85	☐	☐
1880	**1209**	35p multicoloured ..	..	90	90	☐	☐
1881	**1210**	41p multicoloured ..	..	1·00	1·00	☐	☐
		Set of 4		3·00	3·00	☐	☐
		First Day Cover			3·50		☐
		Presentation Pack		3·50		☐	
		PHQ Cards (set of 4)		1·50	4·50	☐	☐
		Set of 4 Gutter Pairs		6·50		☐	

Nos. 1878/81 commemorate the centenary of publication of Wells's *The Time Machine*.

1211 The Swan, 1595

1212 The Rose, 1592

1213 The Globe, 1599

1214 The Hope, 1613

1215 The Globe, 1614

T **1211/15** were printed together, *se-tenant*, in horizontal strips of 5 throughout the sheet, the backgrounds forming a composite design.

Reconstruction of Shakespeare's Globe Theatre

1995 (8 Aug.) *Two phosphor bands. Perf* 14½

1882	**1211**	25p multicoloured	65	65	☐	☐
		a. Horiz strip of 5.				
		Nos. 1882/6	3·00	3·00	☐	☐
1883	**1212**	25p multicoloured	65	65	☐	☐
1884	**1213**	25p multicoloured	65	65	☐	☐
1885	**1214**	25p multicoloured	65	65	☐	☐
1886	**1215**	25p multicoloured	65	65	☐	☐
		Set of 5	3·00	3·00	☐	☐
		First Day Cover		3·25		☐
		Presentation Pack	3·25		☐	
		PHQ Cards (set of 5) ..	1·90	4·75	☐	☐
		Gutter Strip of 10	6·00		☐	

1216 Sir Rowland Hill
and Uniform Penny
Postage Petition

1217 Hill and Penny
Black

1218 Guglielmo Marconi
and Early Wireless

1219 Marconi and
Sinking of *Titanic*
(liner)

Pioneers of Communications

1995 (5 Sept.) *One phosphor band* (19*p.*) *or phosphorised paper* (*others*). *Perf* 14½ × 14

1887	**1216**	19p silver, red and black	55	55	☐	☐
1888	**1217**	25p silver, brown and				
		black	80	80	☐	☐
1889	**1218**	41p silver, grey-green				
		and black	1·10	1·10	☐	☐
1890	**1219**	60p silver, deep ultra-				
		marine and black ..	1·50	1·50	☐	☐
		Set of 4	3·50	3·50	☐	☐
		First Day Cover ..		3·75		☐
		Presentation Pack ..	3·75		☐	
		PHQ Cards (set of				
		4)	1·50	4·75	☐	☐
		Set of 4 Gutter Pairs ..	7·00		☐	

Nos. 1887/8 mark the birth bicentenary of Sir Rowland Hill and Nos. 1889/90 the centenary of the first radio transmissions.

1220 Harold Wagstaff

1221 Gus Risman

1222 Jim Sullivan

1223 Billy Batten

1224 Brian Bevan

Centenary of Rugby League

1995 (3 Oct.) *One phosphor band* (19p) *or two phosphor bands* (*others*). Perf 14 × 14½

1891	**1220**	19p multicoloured	45	45	☐	☐
1892	**1221**	25p multicoloured	60	60	☐	☐
1893	**1222**	30p multicoloured	70	70	☐	☐
1894	**1223**	35p multicoloured	95	95	☐	☐
1895	**1224**	41p multicoloured	1·25	1·25	☐	☐
		Set of 5	3·50	3·50	☐	☐
		First Day Cover		3·75		☐
		Presentation Pack	3·75		☐	
		PHQ Cards (set of 5)	1·90	5·25	☐	☐
		Set of 5 Gutter Pairs	7·00		☐	

1225 European Robin in Mouth of Pillar Box

1226 European Robin on Railings and Holly

1227 European Robin on Snow-covered Milk Bottles

1228 European Robin on Road Sign

1229 European Robin on Door Knob and Christmas Wreath

Christmas. Christmas Robins

1995 (30 Oct.) *One phosphor band* (19p) *or two phosphor bands* (*others*)

1896	**1225**	19p multicoloured	45	45	☐	☐
1897	**1226**	25p multicoloured	60	60	☐	☐
1898	**1227**	30p multicoloured	80	80	☐	☐
1899	**1228**	41p multicoloured	1·10	1·10	☐	☐
1900	**1229**	60p multicoloured	1·50	1·50	☐	☐
		Set of 5	4·00	4·00	☐	☐
		First Day Cover		4·25		☐
		Presentation Pack	4·25		☐	
		PHQ Cards (set of 5)	1·90	5·75	☐	☐
		Set of 5 Gutter Pairs	8·00		☐	

Collectors Pack 1995

1995 (30 Oct.) *Comprises Nos.* 1848/1900.

Collectors Pack	32·00		☐

Post Office Yearbook

1995 (30 Oct.) *Comprises Nos.* 1848/57 *and* 1868/1900 *in hardback book with slip case.*

Yearbook	40·00		☐

1230 Opening Lines of "To a Mouse" and Fieldmouse

1231 "O my Luve's like a red, red rose" and Wild Rose

1232 "Scots, wha hae wi Wallace bled" and Sir William Wallace

1233 "Auld Lang Syne" and Highland Dancers

Death Bicentenary of Robert Burns (Scottish poet)

1996 (25 Jan.) *One phosphor band (19p) or two phosphor bands (others). Perf 14½*

1901	**1230**	19p cream, bistre-brown and black		55	55	☐ ☐
1902	**1231**	25p multicoloured		80	80	☐ ☐
1903	**1232**	41p multicoloured		1·10	1·10	☐ ☐
1904	**1233**	60p multicoloured		1·50	1·50	☐ ☐
		Set of 4		3·50	3·50	☐ ☐
		First Day Cover			3·75	☐
		Presentation Pack		3·75		☐
		PHQ Cards (set of 4)		1·50	4·75	☐ ☐
		Set of 4 Gutter Pairs		7·00		☐

1234 "MORE! LOVE" (Mel Calman)

1235 "Sincerely" (Charles Barsotti)

1236 "Do you have something for the HUMAN CONDITION?" (Mel Calman)

1237 "MENTAL FLOSS" (Leo Cullum)

1238 "4.55 P.M." (Charles Barsotti)

1239 "Dear lottery prize winner" (Larry)

1240 "I'm writing to you because...." (Mel Calman)

1241 "FETCH THIS, FETCH THAT" (Charles Barsotti)

1242 "My day starts before I'm ready for it" (Mel Calman)

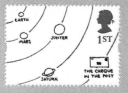

1243 "THE CHEQUE IN THE POST" (Jack Ziegler)

T **1234/43** were printed together, *se-tenant*, in booklet panes of 10 stamps and 20 half stamp-size labels.

Greetings Stamps. Cartoons

1996 (26 Feb-11 Nov) *'All-over' phosphor. Perf 14½ × 14 (with one elliptical hole on each vertical side)*

1905	**1234**	(1st) mauve and bright		40	45	☐ ☐
		a. Booklet pane. Nos. 1905/14		4·00		☐
		p. Two phosphor bands		40	45	☐ ☐
		pa. Booklet pane. Nos. 1905p/14p (11 Nov)		4·00		☐
1906	**1235**	(1st) black and blue-green		40	45	☐ ☐
		p. Two phosphor bands		40	45	☐ ☐
1907	**1236**	(1st) black and new blue		40	45	☐ ☐
		p. Two phosphor bands		40	45	☐ ☐
1908	**1237**	(1st) black and bright violet		40	45	☐ ☐
		p. Two phosphor bands		40	45	☐ ☐
1909	**1238**	(1st) black and vermilion		40	45	☐ ☐
		p. Two phosphor bands		40	45	☐ ☐
1910	**1239**	(1st) black and new blue		40	45	☐ ☐
		p. Two phosphor bands		40	45	☐ ☐
1911	**1240**	(1st) black and vermilion		40	45	☐ ☐
		p. Two phosphor bands		40	45	☐ ☐
1912	**1241**	(1st) black and bright violet		40	45	☐ ☐
		p. Two phosphor bands		40	45	☐ ☐
1913	**1242**	(1st) black and blue-green ..		40	45	☐ ☐
		p. Two phosphor bands		40	45	☐ ☐
1914	**1243**	(1st) black and bright mauve		40	45	☐ ☐
		p. Two phosphor bands		40	45	☐ ☐
		Set of 10 (Nos. 1905/14) ..		4·00	4·50	☐ ☐
		Set of 10 (Nos. 1905p/14p) ..		4·00	4·50	☐ ☐
		First Day Cover (Nos. 1905/14)			6·50	☐
		Presentation Pack		4·25		☐
		PHQ Cards (set of 10)		3·75	8·75	☐ ☐

1244 "Muscovy Duck"

1245 "Lapwing"

1246 "White-fronted Goose"

1247 "Bittern"

1248 "Whooper Swan"

50th Anniversary of the Wildfowl and Wetlands Trust. Bird Paintings by C. F. Tunnicliffe

1996 (12 MAR.) *One phosphor band (19p) or phosphorised paper (others). Perf* $14 \times 14\frac{1}{2}$

1915	**1244**	19p multicoloured	..	40	40	☐ ☐
1916	**1245**	25p multicoloured		60	60	☐ ☐
1917	**1246**	30p multicoloured		70	70	☐ ☐
1918	**1247**	35p multicoloured		95	95	☐ ☐
1919	**1248**	41p multicoloured	..	1·25	1·25	☐ ☐
		Set of 5	.. .. ..	3·50	3·50	☐ ☐
		First Day Cover ..	.. ..		3·75	☐
		Presentation Pack	.. ..	3·75		☐
		PHQ Cards (set of 5)	.. ..	1·90	5·25	☐ ☐
		Set of 5 Gutter Pairs	.. ..	7·00		☐

1249 The Odeon, Harrogate

1250 Laurence Olivier and Vivien Leigh in *Lady Hamilton* (film)

1251 Old Cinema Ticket

1252 Pathé News Still

1253 Cinema Sign, The Odeon, Manchester

Centenary of Cinema

1996 (16 APR.) *One phosphor band (19p) or two phosphor bands (others). Perf* $14 \times 14\frac{1}{2}$

1920	**1249**	19p multicoloured	..	40	40	☐ ☐
1921	**1250**	25p multicoloured		60	60	☐ ☐
1922	**1251**	30p multicoloured		70	70	☐ ☐
1923	**1252**	35p black, red and silver		95	95	☐ ☐
1924	**1253**	41p multicoloured		1·25	1·25	☐ ☐
		Set of 5	.. .. ..	3·50	3·50	☐ ☐
		First Day Cover ..	.. ..		3·75	☐
		Presentation Pack	.. ..	3·75		☐
		PHQ Cards (set of 5)	.. ..	1·90	5·25	☐ ☐
		Set of 5 Gutter Pairs	.. ..	7·00		☐

1254 Dixie Dean

1255 Bobby Moore

1256 Duncan Edwards

1257 Billy Wright

1258 Danny Blanchflower

European Football Championship

1996 (14 MAY). *One phosphor band (19p) or two phosphor bands (others). Perf* $14\frac{1}{2} \times 14$

1925	**1254**	19p multicoloured	..	40	40	☐	☐
1926	**1255**	25p multicoloured	..	60	60	☐	☐
1927	**1256**	35p multicoloured	..	1·10	1·10	☐	☐
1928	**1257**	41p multicoloured	..	1·10	1·10	☐	☐
1929	**1258**	60p multicoloured	..	1·50	1·50	☐	☐
		Set of 5		4·25	4·25	☐	☐
		First Day Cover			4·50		☐
		Presentation Pack		4·50		☐	
		PHQ Cards (set of 5)		1·90	5·75	☐	
		Set of 5 Gutter Pairs		8·50		☐	

1259 Athlete on Starting Blocks

1260 Throwing the Javelin

1261 Basketball

1262 Swimming

1263 Athlete celebrating and Olympic Rings

Olympic and Paralympic Games, Atlanta

1996 (9 JULY) *Two phosphor bands. Perf* $14\frac{1}{2} \times 14$

1930	**1259**	26p multicoloured	..	65	65	☐	☐
		a. Horiz strip of 5.					
		Nos. 1930/4	..	3·00	3·00	☐	☐
1931	**1260**	26p multicoloured	..	65	65	☐	☐
1932	**1261**	26p multicoloured	..	65	65	☐	☐
1933	**1262**	26p multicoloured	..	65	65	☐	☐
1934	**1263**	26p multicoloured	..	65	65	☐	☐
		Set of 5		3·00	3·00	☐	☐
		First Day Cover			3·25		☐
		Presentation Pack		3·25		☐	
		PHQ Cards (set of 5)		1·90	4·75	☐	☐
		Gutter Strip of 10		6·00		☐	

1264 Prof. Dorothy Hodgkin (scientist)

1265 Dame Margot Fonteyn (ballerina)

1266 Dame Elisabeth Frink (sculptress)

1267 Dame Daphne du Maurier (novelist)

1268 Dame Marea Hartman (sports administrator)

Europa. Famous Women

1996 (6 AUG.) *One phosphor band (20p) or two phosphor bands (others). Perf* $14\frac{1}{2}$.

1935	**1264**	20p dull blue-green, brownish grey and black	50	50	☐	☐
1936	**1265**	26p dull mauve, brownish grey and black	70	70	☐	☐

Nos. 1930/4 were printed together, *se-tenant*, in horizontal strips of 5 throughout the sheet.

1937	**1266**	31p bronze, brownish grey and black	..	90	90	☐ ☐
1938	**1267**	37p silver, brownish grey and black	..	1·10	1·10	☐ ☐
1939	**1268**	43p gold, brownish grey and black	..	1·25	1·25	☐ ☐
		Set of 5		4·00	4·00	☐ ☐
		First Day Cover			4·25	☐
		Presentation Pack		4·25		☐
		PHQ Cards (set of 5)		1·90	5·25	☐ ☐
		Set of 5 Gutter Pairs		8·00		☐

Nos. 1936/7 include the "EUROPA" emblem.

1269 Muffin the Mule

1270 Sooty

1271 Stingray

1272 The Clangers

1273 Dangermouse

50th Anniversary of Children's Television

1996 (3 SEPT.)–**97** One phosphor band (20p) or two phosphor bands (others). Perf $14\frac{1}{2} \times 14$

1940	**1269**	20p multicoloured	..	50	50	☐ ☐
		a. Perf 15×14		1·00	1·00	☐ ☐
1941	**1270**	26p multicoloured	..	70	70	☐ ☐
1942	**1271**	31p multicoloured	..	90	90	☐ ☐
1943	**1272**	37p multicoloured	..	1·10	1·10	☐ ☐
1944	**1273**	43p multicoloured	..	1·25	1·25	☐ ☐
		Set of 5		4·00	4·00	☐ ☐
		First Day Cover			4·25	☐
		Presentation Pack		4·25		☐
		PHQ Cards (set of 5)		1·90	5·25	☐ ☐
		Set of 5 Gutter Pairs		8·00		☐

No. 1940a comes from booklets.

1274 Triumph TR3

1275 MG TD

1276 Austin-Healey 100

1277 Jaguar XK120

1278 Morgan Plus 4

Classic Sports Cars

1996 (1 OCT.) One phosphor band (20p) or two phosphor bands (others). Perf $14\frac{1}{2}$

1945	**1274**	20p multicoloured	..	40	40	☐ ☐
1946	**1275**	26p multicoloured	..	55	55	☐ ☐
1947	**1276**	37p multicoloured	..	75	75	☐ ☐
1948	**1277**	43p multicoloured	..	90	90	☐ ☐
1949	**1278**	63p multicoloured	..	1·25	1·25	☐ ☐
		Set of 5		3·50	3·50	☐ ☐
		First Day Cover			3·75	☐
		Presentation Pack		3·75		☐
		PHQ Cards (set of 5)		1·90	5·75	☐ ☐
		Set of 5 Gutter Pairs		7·00		☐

1279 The Three Kings

1280 The Annunciation

1281 The Journey to Bethlehem

1282 The Nativity

1283 The Shepherds

1286 *Camellia japonica* (Alfred Chandler)

1287 *Tulipa* (Ehret)

1288 *Fuchsia "Princess of Wales"* (Augusta Withers)

1289 *Tulipa gesneriana* (Ehret)

1290 *Guzmania splendens* (Charlotte Sowerby)

1291 *Iris latifolia* (Ehret)

1292 *Hippeastrum rutilum* (Pierre-Joseph Redouté)

1293 *Passiflora coerulea* (Ehret)

Christmas

1996 (28 Oct.) *One phosphor band* (2nd *class*) *or two phosphor bands* (*others*)

1950	**1279**	(2nd) multicoloured	..	40	40	□ □
1951	**1280**	(1st) multicoloured	..	55	55	□ □
1952	**1281**	31p multicoloured	..	65	65	□ □
1953	**1282**	43p multicoloured	..	90	90	□ □
1954	**1283**	63p multicoloured	..	1·25	1·25	□ □
	Set of 5	.. ..		3·25	3·25	□ □
	First Day Cover				3·50	□
	Presentation Pack	.. ..		3·50		□
	PHQ Cards (set of 5)	.. ..		1·90	5·50	□ □
	Set of 5 Gutter Pairs	.. ..		6·50		□

Collectors Pack 1996

1996 (28 Oct.) *Comprises Nos.* 1901/4 *and* 1915/54

Collectors Pack ..	.. ..	30·00	□

Post Office Yearbook

1996 (28 Oct.) *Comprises Nos.* 1901/4 *and* 1915/54 *in hardback book with slip case.*

Yearbook	40·00		□

1284 *Gentiana acaulis* (Georg Ehret)

1285 *Magnolia grandiflora* (Ehret)

T **1284/93** were printed together, *se-tenant*, in booklet panes of 10 stamps and 20 half stamp-size labels.

Greeting Stamps. 19th-century Flower Paintings

1997 (6 Jan.) *Two phosphor bands. Perf* $14\frac{1}{2} \times 14$ (*with one elliptical hole on each vertical side*)

1955	**1284**	(1st) multicoloured..	..	40	45	□ □
		a. Booklet pane. Nos.				
		1955/64		4·00		□
1956	**1285**	(1st) multicoloured..	..	40	45	□ □
1957	**1286**	(1st) multicoloured..	..	40	45	□ □
1958	**1287**	(1st) multicoloured..	..	40	45	□ □
1959	**1288**	(1st) multicoloured..	..	40	45	□ □
1960	**1289**	(1st) multicoloured..	..	40	45	□ □
1961	**1290**	(1st) multicoloured..	..	40	45	□ □
1962	**1291**	(1st) multicoloured..	..	40	45	□ □

1963	**1292**	(1st) multicoloured			40	45	□ □
1964	**1293**	(1st) multicoloured			40	45	□ □
		Set of 10	..	..	4·00	4·50	□ □
		First Day Cover	..	..		7·50	□ □
		Presentation Pack	..	..	4·50		□
		PHQ Cards (set of 10)	..	..	2·50	7·50	□ □

1294 "King Henry VIII"

1295 "Catherine of Aragon"

1296 "Anne Boleyn"

1297 "Jane Seymour"

1298 "Anne of Cleves"

1299 "Catherine Howard"

1300 "Catherine Parr"

T 1295/1300 were printed together, *se-tenant*, in horizontal strips of 6 throughout the sheet.

450th Death Anniv of King Henry VIII

1997 (21 Jan.) *Two phosphor bands. Perf 15 (No. 1965) 14 × 15 (others)*

1965	**1294**	26p multicoloured		40	45	□
1966	**1295**	26p multicoloured		40	45	□
		a. Horiz strip of 6.				
		Nos. 1966/71	..	2·75	3·00	□
1967	**1296**	26p multicoloured		40	45	□
1968	**1297**	26p multicoloured		40	45	□
1969	**1298**	26p multicoloured		40	45	□
1970	**1299**	26p multicoloured		40	45	□
1971	**1300**	26p multicoloured		40	45	□
		Set of 7	.. .. ..	2·75	3·25	□
		First Day Cover ..	.. ..		4·25	□
		Presentation Pack	.. ..	3·25		□
		PHQ Cards (set of 7)	.. ..	2·50	5·50	□
		Gutter Pair and Gutter Block of				
		12		5·75	6·75	□

1301 St. Columba in Boat

1302 St. Columba on Iona

1303 St. Augustine with King Ethelbert

1304 St. Augustine with Model of Cathedral

Religious Anniversaries

1997 (11 Mar.) *Two phosphor bands. Perf 14½*

1972	**1301**	26p multicoloured	40	45	□
1973	**1302**	37p multicoloured	60	65	□
1974	**1303**	43p multicoloured	65	70	□
1975	**1304**	63p multicoloured	95	1·00	□
		Set of 4	2·50	2·75	□
		First Day Cover		4·25	□
		Presentation Pack	3·00		□
		PHQ Cards (set of 4)	1·50	4·25	□
		Set of 4 Gutter Pairs..	5·25	5·75	□

Nos. 1972/3 commemorate the 1400th death anniversa of St. Columba and Nos. 1974/5 the 1400th anniversary the arrival of St. Augustine of Canterbury in Kent.

305

1306

elf-adhesive Coil Stamps

997 (18 Mar.) *Photo Enschedé. One centre phosphor band nd) or two phosphor bands (1st). Perf 14 × 15 die-cut with one elliptical hole on each vertical side).*

076	**1305**	(2nd) bright blue	..	..	50	50	☐ ☐
077	**1306**	(1st) bright orange-red	..		40	45	☐ ☐
		Set of 2	..	.. .. ..	90	95	☐ ☐
		First Day Cover	..	.. ..		1·75	☐
		Presentation Pack	..	.. ..	1·40		☐

Nos. 1976/7, which were initially priced at 20p. and 26p, ere each sold in rolls of 100 with the stamps separate on the ocking paper.

oyal Golden Wedding

997 (21 Apr.) *Designs as T 369 and 917 but colours nanged. Printed in photogravure by Harrison (26p), arrison or Walsall (1st). Perf 15 × 14 (with one elliptical le on each vertical edge)*

078	**369**	26p gold	..	.. ..	40	45	☐ ☐
079	**917**	(1st) gold	..	.. ..	40	45	☐ ☐
		Set of 2	..	.. ..	80	90	☐ ☐
		First Day Cover	..	.. ..		2·50	☐
		Presentation Pack	..	.. ..	1·40		☐

Dracula

07 *Dracula*

31

Frankenstein

1308 *Frankenstein*

Dr Jekyll and Mr Hyde

09 *Dr. Jekyll and Mr. Hyde*

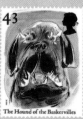

43

The Hound of the Baskervilles

1310 *The Hound of the Baskervilles*

Tales and Legends, Horror Stories

1997 (13 May) *Two phosphor bands. Perf 14 × 15*

1980	**1307**	26p multicoloured..	..	40	45	☐ ☐
1981	**1308**	31p multicoloured..	..	50	55	☐ ☐
1982	**1309**	37p multicoloured..	..	60	65	☐ ☐
1983	**1310**	43p multicoloured..	..	65	70	☐ ☐
		Set of 4	.. ..	2·10	2·25	☐ ☐
		First Day Cover ..	.. ..		3·50	☐
		Presentation Pack	.. .. ..	2·50		☐
		PHQ Cards (set of 4)	.. ..	1·50	4·50	☐ ☐
		Set of 4 Gutter Pairs..	.. ..	4·50		☐

Nos. 1980/3 commemorate the birth bicentenary of Mary Shelley (creator of Frankenstein) with the 26p. and 31p. values incorporating the "EUROPA" emblem.

1311 Reginald Mitchell and Supermarine Spitfire MkIIA

1312 Roy Chadwick and Avro Lancaster MkI

1313 Ronald Bishop and De Havilland Mosquito B MkXVI

1314 George Carter and Gloster Meteor F Mk8

1315 Sir Sidney Camm and Hawker Hunter FGA Mk9

British Aircraft Designers

1997 (10 June) *One phosphor band (20p) or two phosphor bands (others).*

1984	**1311**	20p multicoloured..	..	30	35	☐ ☐
1985	**1312**	26p multicoloured..	..	40	45	☐ ☐
1986	**1313**	37p multicoloured..	..	60	65	☐ ☐
1987	**1314**	43p multicoloured..	..	65	70	☐ ☐
1988	**1315**	63p multicoloured..	..	95	1·00	☐ ☐
		Set of 5	.. ..	2·75	3·00	☐ ☐
		First Day Cover ..	.. ..		4·50	☐
		Presentation Pack	.. ..	3·25		☐
		PHQ Cards ..	.. .. ..	1·90	6·00	☐ ☐
		Set of 5 Gutter Pairs..	.. ..	5·75		☐

1316 Carriage Horse and Coachman

1317 Lifeguards Horse and Trooper

1318 Household Cavalry Drum Horse and Drummer

1319 Duke of Edinburgh's Horse and Groom

"All the Queen's Horses". 50th Anniv of the British Horse Society

1997 (8 JULY) One phosphor band (20p) or two phosphor bands (others). Perf 14½

1989	**1316**	20p multicoloured		30	35	☐ ☐
1990	**1317**	26p multicoloured		40	45	☐ ☐
1991	**1318**	43p multicoloured		65	70	☐ ☐
1992	**1319**	63p multicoloured		95	1·00	☐ ☐
		Set of 4		2·25	2·50	☐ ☐
		First Day Cover			3·50	☐
		Presentation Pack		2·75		☐
		PHQ Cards (set of 4)		1·50	4·75	☐ ☐
		Set of 4 Gutter Pairs		4·75		☐

CASTLE Harrison printing (Nos. 1611/14)

CASTLE Enschedé printing (Nos. 1993/6)

Differences between Harrison and Enschedé printings:
Harrison - "C" has top serif and tail of letter points to right. "A" has flat top. "S" has top and bottom serifs.
Enschedé - "C" has no top serif and tail of letter points upwards. "A" has pointed top. "S" has no serifs.

1997 (29 JULY) Designs as Nos. 1612/14 with Queen's head in silhouette as T **1044**, but re-engraved as above, Perf 15 × 14 (with one elliptical hole on each vertical side).

1993	**882**	£1·50 deep claret and gold†		2·25	2·40	☐ ☐
1994	**883**	£2 indigo and gold†		3·00	3·25	☐ ☐
1995	**1048**	£3 violet and gold†		4·50	4·75	☐ ☐
1996	**884**	£5 deep brown and gold†		7·50	7·75	☐ ☐
		Set of 4		17·00	18·00	☐ ☐
		Set of 4 Gutter Pairs		35·00		☐

† The Queen's head on these stamps is printed in optically variable ink which changes colour from gold to green when viewed from different angles.

1320 Haroldswick, Shetland

1321 Painswick, Gloucestershire

1322 Beddgelert, Gwynedd

1323 Ballyroney, County Down

Sub-Post Offices

1997 (12 AUG.) One phosphor band (20p) or two phosphor bands (others). Perf 14½

1997	**1320**	20p multicoloured		30	35	☐ ☐
1998	**1321**	26p multicoloured		40	45	☐ ☐
1999	**1322**	43p multicoloured		65	70	☐ ☐
2000	**1323**	63p multicoloured		95	1·00	☐ ☐
		Set of 4		2·25	2·50	☐ ☐
		First Day Cover			3·50	☐
		Presentation Pack		2·75		☐
		PHQ Cards (Set of 4)		1·50	4·75	☐ ☐
		Set of 4 Gutter Pairs		4·75		☐

Nos. 1997/2000 also mark the Centenary of the National Federation of Sub-Postmasters.

Enid Blyton's *Noddy*

1324 Noddy

Enid Blyton's *Famous Five*

1325 Famous Five

Enid Blyton's *Secret Seven*

326 Secret Seven

Enid Blyton's *Faraway Tree*

1327 Faraway Tree

Enid Blyton's *Malory Towers*

1328 Malory Towers

irth Centenary of Enid Blyton (children's author)

997 (9 Sept.) *One phosphor band (20p) or two phosphor
ands (others). Perf* 14 × 14½

001	**1324**	20p multicoloured..	..	30	35	☐	☐
002	**1325**	26p multicoloured..	..	40	45	☐	☐
003	**1326**	37p multicoloured..	..	60	65	☐	☐
004	**1327**	43p multicoloured..	..	65	70	☐	☐
005	**1328**	63p multicoloured..	..	95	1·00	☐	☐
		Set of 5	.. ..	2·75	3·00	☐	☐
		First Day Cover ..	.. ..		4·00		☐
		Presentation Pack	.. ..	3·25		☐	
		PHQ Cards (set of 5)	.. ..	1·90	5·75	☐	☐
		Set of 5 Gutter Pairs..	.. ..	5·75		☐	

329 Children and Father
Christmas pulling Cracker

331 Father Christmas riding
Cracker

1330 Father Christmas with
Traditional Cracker

1332 Father Christmas on
Snowball

1333 Father Christmas and
Chimney

Christmas. 150th Anniv of the Christmas Cracker

1997 (27 Oct) *One phosphor band (2nd class) or two
phosphor bands (others).*

2006	**1329**	(2nd) multicoloured..	..	30	35	☐	☐
2007	**1330**	(1st) multicoloured..	..	40	45	☐	☐
2008	**1331**	31p multicoloured..	..	50	55	☐	☐
2009	**1332**	43p multicoloured..	..	65	70	☐	☐
2010	**1333**	63p multicoloured..	..	95	1·00	☐	☐
		Set of 5	.. ..	2·75	3·00	☐	☐
		First Day Cover ..	.. ..		4·00		☐
		Presentation Pack	.. ..	3·25		☐	
		PHQ Cards (set of 5)	.. ..	1·90	5·75	☐	☐
		Set of 5 Gutter Pairs..	.. ..	5·75		☐	

1334 Wedding Photograph,
1947

1335 Queen Elizabeth II and
Prince Philip, 1997

Royal Golden Wedding (2nd issue)

1997 (13 Nov.) *One phosphor band (20p) or two phosphor
bands (others). Perf* 15

2011	**1334**	20p gold, yellow-brown and grey-black	..	30	35	☐	☐
2012	**1335**	26p multicoloured..	..	40	45	☐	☐
2013	**1334**	43p gold, bluish green and grey-black	..	65	70	☐	☐
2014	**1335**	63p multicoloured..	..	95	1·00	☐	☐
		Set of 4	.. ..	2·25	2·50	☐	☐
		First Day Cover ..	.. ..		3·25		☐
		Presentation Pack	.. ..	2·75		☐	
		Souvenir Book (contains Nos. 1979, 1989/92 and 2011/14)	.. ..	15·00		☐	
		PHQ Cards (set of 4)	.. ..	1·50	4·75	☐	☐
		Set of 4 Gutter Pairs..	.. ..	4·75		☐	

Collectors Pack 1997

1997 (27 Oct) *Comprises Nos. 1965/75, 1980/92 and
1997/2014*

	Collectors Pack	24·00	☐

Post Office Yearbook

1997 (27 Oct.) *Comprises Nos. 1965/75, 1980/92 and
1997/2014 in hardback book with slip case*

	Yearbook	35·00	☐

Keep this catalogue up to date each month with...

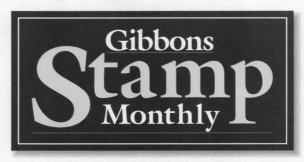

The leading magazine for Great Britain collectors since 1890 and the only magazine containing the Stanley Gibbons catalogue supplement.

Exceptional value for money.

50% more editorial than other magazines.

Authoritatively written by active stamp collectors.

Regular features for all collectors from beginners to specialist.

Includes the unique Stanley Gibbons catalogue supplement.

Exclusive British Stamps and GB specialised catalogue supplement.

Special features are devoted to new issues, covers, Machins, books, auctions and fairs.

Monthly competition and frequent free gifts.

DELIVERED DIRECT TO YOUR DOOR!

Get **Gibbons Stamp Monthly** delivered to your door each month, Post Free to all UK addresses. As a subscriber you will also get exclusive access to additional special offers on Stanley Gibbons products.

For a free sample copy and subscription details phone 0800 611622 today or write to:
GIBBONS STAMP MONTHLY,
5 Parkside, Christchurch Road, Ringwood, Hants BH24 3SH England.
Telephone: 01425 472363   Facsimile: 01425 470247
e.mail: sales@stangib.demon.co.uk

PERFORATION AND WATERMARK. All the following Regional stamps are perforated 15 × 14 and are watermarked Type **179**, unless otherwise stated.
For listing of First Day Covers see pages 134/5.

▌Northern Ireland

	N 1		N 2		N 3		N 4

1958–67

NI1	N 1	3d lilac	20	10	☐ ☐
	p	One centre phosphor band	20	15	☐ ☐
NI2		4d blue	20	15	☐ ☐
	p	Two phosphor bands	20	15	☐ ☐
NI3	N 2	6d purple	20	20	☐ ☐
NI4		9d bronze-green (2 phosphor bands)	30	70	☐ ☐
NI5	N 3	1s 3d green	30	70	☐ ☐
NI6		1s 6d blue (2 phosphor bands)	30	70	☐ ☐

1968–69 One centre phosphor band (Nos. NI8/9) or two phosphor bands (others). No wmk

NI7	N 1	4d blue	20	15	☐ ☐
NI8		4d sepia	20	15	☐ ☐
NI9		4d vermilion	20	20	☐ ☐
NI10		5d blue	20	20	☐ ☐
NI11	N 3	1s 6d blue	2·50	3·25	☐
		Presentation Pack (comprises Nos NI1p, NI4/6, NI8/10)	3·25		☐

Decimal Currency

1971–91 Type N 4. No wmk

(a) Printed in photogravure with phosphor bands

NI12	2½p magenta (1 centre band)	80	25	☐ ☐
NI13	3p ultramarine (2 bands)	40	15	☐ ☐
NI14	3p ultramarine (1 centre band)	20	15	☐ ☐
NI15	3½p olive-grey (2 bands)	20	20	☐ ☐
NI16	3½p olive-grey (1 centre band)	20	25	☐ ☐
NI17	4½p grey-blue (2 bands)	25	25	☐ ☐
NI18	5p violet (2 bands)	1·50	1·50	☐ ☐
NI19	5½p violet (2 bands)	20	20	☐ ☐
NI20	5½p violet (1 centre band)	20	20	☐ ☐
NI21	6½p blue (1 centre band)	20	20	☐ ☐
NI22	7p brown (1 centre band)	35	25	☐ ☐
NI23	7½p chestnut (2 bands)	2·25	2·25	☐ ☐

NI24	8p rosine (2 bands)	30	30	☐ ☐
NI25	8½p yellow-green (2 bands)	30	30	☐ ☐
NI26	9p violet (2 bands)	30	30	☐ ☐
NI27	10p orange-brown (2 bands)	35	35	☐ ☐
NI28	10p orange-brown (1 centre band)	35	35	☐ ☐
NI29	10½p blue (2 bands)	50	50	☐ ☐
NI30	11p scarlet (2 bands)	50	50	☐ ☐

(b) Printed in photogravure on phosphorised paper

NI31	12p yellowish green	50	50	☐ ☐
NI32	13½p purple-brown	70	80	☐ ☐
NI33	15p ultramarine	70	70	☐ ☐

(c) Printed in lithography. Perf 14 (11½p, 12½p, 14p (No. NI38), 15½p, 16p, 18p (No. NI45), 19½p, 20½p, 22p (No. NI53), 26p (No. NI60), 28p (No. NI62)) or 15 × 14 (others)

NI34	11½p drab (1 side band)	70	70	☐ ☐
NI35	12p brt emer (1 side band)	70	70	☐ ☐
NI36	12½p light emer (1 side band)	60	60	☐ ☐
	a. Perf 15 × 14	4·25	4·25	☐ ☐
NI37	13p pale chest (1 side band)	1·25	70	☐ ☐
NI38	14p grey-blue (phosphorised paper)	70	60	☐ ☐
NI39	14p dp blue (1 centre band)	70	60	☐ ☐
NI40	15p brt blue (1 centre band)	70	60	☐ ☐
NI41	15½p pale violet (phosphorised paper)	80	65	☐ ☐
NI42	16p drab (phosphorised paper)	1·00	1·00	☐ ☐
	a. Perf 15 × 14	9·50	8·00	☐ ☐
NI43	17p grey-blue (phosphorised paper)	1·00	80	☐ ☐
NI44	17p deep blue (1 centre band)	70	70	☐ ☐
NI45	18p dp violet (phosphorised paper)	90	90	☐ ☐
NI46	18p olive-grey (phosphorised paper)	80	80	☐ ☐
NI47	18p brt grn (1 centre band)	70	70	☐ ☐
	a. Perf 14	1·25	1·25	☐ ☐
NI48	18p brt grn (1 side band)	2·00	2·00	☐ ☐
NI49	19p bright orange-red (phosphorised paper)	80	70	☐ ☐
NI50	19½p olive-grey (phosphorised paper)	1·75	2·25	☐ ☐
NI51	20p brownish black (phosphorised paper)	80	70	☐ ☐
NI52	20½p ultramarine (phosphorised paper)	4·00	4·00	☐ ☐
NI53	22p blue (phosphorised paper)	1·00	1·10	☐ ☐
NI54	22p yellow-green (phosphorised paper)	1·00	1·10	☐ ☐
NI55	22p bright orange-red (phosphorised paper)	1·00	85	☐ ☐
NI56	23p bright green (phosphorised paper)	1·00	1·10	☐ ☐
NI57	24p Indian red (phosphorised paper)	1·00	1·10	☐ ☐
NI58	24p chestnut (phosphorised paper)	90	75	☐ ☐
NI59	24p chestnut (2 bands)	2·00	2·00	☐ ☐

NI60	26p rosine (phosphorised paper)	1·10	1·40	☐	☐
	a. Perf 15 × 14	2·00	2·00	☐	☐
NI61	26p drab (phosphorised paper)	1·00	1·00	☐	☐
NI62	28p deep violet-blue (phosphorised paper)	1·10	1·10	☐	☐
	a. Perf 15 × 14	1·10	1·10	☐	☐
NI63	28p deep bluish grey (phosphorised paper)	1·10	1·10	☐	☐
NI64	31p bright purple (phosphorised paper)	1·40	1·40	☐	☐
NI65	32p greenish blue (phosphorised paper)	1·25	1·25	☐	☐
NI66	34p deep bluish grey (phosphorised paper)	1·40	1·40	☐	☐
NI67	37p rosine (phosphorised paper)	1·40	1·40	☐	☐
NI68	39p bright mauve (phosphorised paper)	1·40	1·40	☐	☐

Presentation Pack (contains 2½p (NI12), 3p (NI13), 5p, (NI18), 7½p (NI23)) ... 4·25 ☐

Presentation Pack (contains 3p (NI14), 3½p (NI15), 5½p (NI19), 8p (NI24) later with 4½p (NI17) added) ... 2·50 ☐

Presentation Pack (contains 6½p (NI21), 8½p (NI25), 10p (NI27), 11p (NI30)) ... 2·00 ☐

Presentation Pack (contains 7p (NI22), 9p (NI26), 10½p (NI29), 11½p (NI34), 12p (NI31), 13½p (NI32), 14p (NI38), 15p (NI33), 18p (NI45), 22p (NI53)) ... 7·50 ☐

Presentation Pack (contains 10p (NI28), 12½p (NI36), 16p (NI42), 20½p (NI52), 26p (NI60), 28p (NI62)) ... 7·50 ☐

Presentation Pack (contains 10p (NI28), 13p (NI37), 16p (NI42a), 17p (NI43), 22p (NI54), 26p (NI60), 28p (NI62), 31p (NI64)) ... 12·00 ☐

Presentation Pack (contains 12p (NI35), 13p (NI37), 17p (NI43), 18p (NI46), 22p (NI54), 26p (NI60a), 28p (NI62a), 31p (NI64)) ... 7·50 ☐

Presentation Pack (contains 14p, 19p, 23p, 32p from Northern Ireland, Scotland and Wales (Nos. NI39, NI49, NI56, NI65, S54, S62, S67, S77, W40, W50, W57, W66)) ... 8·00 ☐

Presentation Pack (contains 15p, 20p, 24p, 34p from Northern Ireland, Scotland and Wales (Nos. NI40, NI51, NI57, NI66, S56, S64, S69, S78, W41, W52, W58, W67)) ... 8·00 ☐

Presentation Pack (contains 17p, 22p, 26p, 37p, from Northern Ireland, Scotland and Wales (Nos. NI44, NI55, NI61, NI67, S58, S66, S73, S79, W45, W56, W62, W68)) ... 8·00 ☐

Presentation Pack (contains 18p, 24p, 28p, 39p from Northern Ireland, Scotland and Wales (Nos. NI47, NI58, NI63, NI68, S60, S70, S75, S80, W48, W59, W64, W69)) ... 6·00 ☐

Nos. NI48 and NI59 come from booklets.

1993 (7 Dec)-**97**. *Perf* 15 × 14 *(with one elliptical hole on each vertical side)*

(a) Printed in lithography by Questa.

NI69	N 4	19p bistre (1 centre band)	40	40	☐	☐
NI70		19p bistre (1 side band)	2·25	2·25	☐	☐
NI71		20p bright green (1 centre band)	30	35	☐	☐
NI72		25p red (2 bands)	50	50	☐	☐
NI73		26p red-brown (2 bands)	40	45	☐	☐
NI74		30p deep olive-grey (2 bands)	60	60	☐	☐
NI75		37p bright mauve (2 bands)	60	65	☐	☐
NI76		41p grey-brown (2 bands)	90	90	☐	☐
NI77		63p light emerald (2 bands)	95	1·00	☐	☐

(b) Printed in photogravure by Walsall (20p, 63p), or Harrison or Walsall (26p, 37p)

NI78	N 4	20p bright green (1 centre band)	30	35	☐	☐
NI79		26p chestnut (2 bands)	40	45	☐	☐
NI80		37p bright mauve (2 bands)	60	65	☐	☐
NI81		63p light emerald (2 bands)	95	1·00	☐	☐

Presentation Pack (contains 19p, 25p, 30p, 41p from Northern Ireland, Scotland and Wales (Nos. NI69, NI72, NI74, NI76, S81, S84, S86, S88, W70, W73, W75, W77)) ... 8·00 ☐

Presentation Pack (contains 20p, 26p, 37p, 63p from Northern Ireland, Scotland and Wales (Nos. NI71, NI73, NI75, NI77, S83, S85, S87, S89, W72, W74, W76, W78)) ... 7·00 ☐

No. NI70 was only issued in booklets. It exists with the phosphor band at the left or right of the stamp.

2 Scotland

S 1	S 2	S 3	S 4

1958–67

S1	S 1	3d	lilac	20	15	☐ ☐
		p	Two phosphor bands	13·00	1·25	☐ ☐
		pa	One side band	20	25	☐ ☐
		pb	One centre band	20	15	☐ ☐
S2		4d	blue	20	10	☐ ☐
		p	Two phosphor bands	20	20	☐ ☐
S3	S 2	6d	purple	20	15	☐ ☐
		p	Two phosphor bands	20	25	☐ ☐
S4		9d	bronze-green (2 phosphor bands)	30	30	☐ ☐
S5	S 3	1s 3d	green	30	30	☐ ☐
		p	Two phosphor bands	30	30	☐ ☐
S6		1s 6d	blue (2 phosphor bands)	35	30	☐ ☐

No. S1*pa* exists with the phosphor band at the left or right of the stamp.

1967–70 *One centre phosphor band (Nos S7, S9/10) or two phosphor bands (others) No wmk*

S7	S 1	3d	lilac	10	15	☐ ☐
S8		4d	blue	10	15	☐ ☐
S9		4d	sepia	10	10	☐ ☐
S10		4d	vermilion	10	10	☐ ☐
S11		5d	blue	20	10	☐ ☐
S12	S 2	9d	bronze-green	5·00	6·50	☐ ☐
S13	S 3	1s 6d	blue	1·40	1·00	☐ ☐
			Presentation Pack (containing Nos. S3, S5p, S7, S9/13)	10·00		☐

Decimal Currency

1971–93 *Type S 4. No wmk*

(a) Printed in photogravure by Harrison and Sons with phosphor bands. Perf. 15 × 14.

S14	2½p	magenta (1 centre band)	25	15	☐ ☐
S15	3p	ultramarine (2 bands)	30	15	☐ ☐
S16	3p	ultramarine (1 centre band)	15	15	☐ ☐
S17	3½p	olive-grey (2 bands)	20	20	☐ ☐
S18	3½p	ol-grey (1 centre band)	20	20	☐ ☐
S19	4½p	grey-blue (2 bands)	25	20	☐ ☐
S20	5p	violet (2 bands)	1·00	1·00	☐ ☐
S21	5½p	violet (2 bands)	20	20	☐ ☐
S22	5½p	violet (1 centre band)	20	20	☐ ☐
S23	6½p	blue (1 centre band)	20	20	☐ ☐
S24	7p	brown (1 centre band)	25	25	☐ ☐
S25	7½p	chestnut (2 bands)	1·25	1·25	☐ ☐
S26	8p	rosine (2 bands)	30	40	☐ ☐
S27	8½p	yellow-green (2 bands)	30	30	☐ ☐
S28	9p	violet (2 bands)	30	30	☐ ☐
S29	10p	orange-brown (2 bands)	35	30	☐ ☐
S30	10p	orange-brown (1 centre band)	35	35	☐ ☐
S31	10½p	blue (2 bands)	50	35	☐ ☐
S32	11p	scarlet (2 bands)	50	35	☐ ☐

(b) Printed in photogravure by Harrison and Sons on phosphorised paper. Perf 15 × 14

S33	12p	yellowish green	50	30	☐ ☐
S34	13½p	purple-brown	70	65	☐ ☐
S35	15p	ultramarine	60	45	☐ ☐

(c) Printed in lithography by John Waddington. One side phosphor band (11½p, 12p, 12½p, 13p) or phosphorised paper (others). Perf. 14

S36	11½p	drab	80	60	☐ ☐
S37	12p	bright emerald	1·75	1·50	☐ ☐
S38	12½p	light emerald	60	50	☐ ☐
S39	13p	pale chestnut	70	50	☐ ☐
S40	14p	grey-blue	60	50	☐ ☐
S41	15½p	pale violet	70	65	☐ ☐
S42	16p	drab	70	55	☐ ☐
S43	17p	grey-blue	3·50	2·25	☐ ☐
S44	18p	deep violet	80	80	☐ ☐
S45	19½p	olive-grey	1·75	1·75	☐ ☐
S46	20½p	ultramarine	4·00	4·00	☐ ☐
S47	22p	blue	90	1·25	☐ ☐
S48	22p	yellow-green	2·25	2·00	☐ ☐
S49	26p	rosine	1·10	1·25	☐ ☐
S50	28p	deep violet-blue	1·10	1·10	☐ ☐
S51	31p	bright purple	2·00	1·75	☐ ☐

(d) Printed in lithography by Questa. Perf 15 × 14

S52	12p	brt emer (1 side band)	2·00	1·75	☐ ☐
S53	13p	pale chest (1 side band)	70	50	☐ ☐
S54	14p	dp blue (1 centre band)	50	50	☐ ☐
S55	14p	deep blue (1 side band)	80	1·00	☐ ☐
S56	15p	bright blue (1 centre band)	70	55	☐ ☐
S57	17p	grey-blue (phosphorised paper)	4·25	2·25	☐ ☐
S58	17p	dp blue (1 centre band)	60	60	☐ ☐
S59	18p	olive-grey (phosphorised paper)	80	80	☐ ☐
S60	18p	brt green (1 centre band)	70	70	☐ ☐
		a. Perf 14	1·00	75	☐ ☐
S61	18p	brt grn (1 side band)	2·00	2·00	☐ ☐
S62	19p	bright orange-red (phosphorised paper)	80	65	☐ ☐
S63	19p	brt orange-red (2 bands)	1·50	1·50	☐ ☐
S64	20p	brownish black (phosphorised paper)	80	60	☐ ☐
S65	22p	yell-grn (phosphorised paper)	90	90	☐ ☐
S66	22p	bright orange-red (phosphorised paper)	1·00	75	☐ ☐
S67	23p	brt green (phosphorised paper)	1·00	1·10	☐ ☐
S68	23p	bright green (2 bands)	12·00	11·00	☐ ☐

S69	24p Indian red (phosphorised paper)	1·00	1·00	☐	☐
S70	24p chestnut (phosphorised paper)	75	75	☐	☐
	a. Perf 14	1·50	1·25	☐	☐
S71	24p chestnut (2 bands)	2·00	2·00	☐	☐
S72	26p rosine (phosphorised paper)	2·50	2·50	☐	☐
S73	26p drab (phosphorised paper)	1·00	1·00	☐	☐
S74	28p deep violet-blue (phosphorised paper)	1·10	1·10	☐	☐
S75	28p deep bluish grey (phosphorised paper)	1·10	1·10	☐	☐
	a. Perf 14	1·75	1·75	☐	☐
S76	31p bright purple (phosphorised paper)	1·75	1·75	☐	☐
S77	32p greenish blue (phosphorised paper)	1·25	1·25	☐	☐
S78	34p deep bluish grey (phosphorised paper)	1·40	1·40	☐	☐
S79	37p rosine (phosphorised paper)	1·40	1·40	☐	☐
S80	39p bright mauve (phosphorised paper)	1·40	1·40	☐	☐
	a. Perf 14	2·25	2·25	☐	☐

Presentation Pack (*contains* 2½p (S14), 3p (S15), 5p (S20), 7½p (S25))	4·25	☐
Presentation Pack (*contains* 3p (S16), 3½p (S17), 5½p (S21), 8p (S26) *later with* 4½p (S19) *added*)	2·50	☐
Presentation Pack (*contains* 6½p (S23), 8½p (S27), 10p (S29), 11p (S32))	2·00	☐
Presentation Pack (*contains* 7p (S24), 9p (S28), 10½p (S31), 11½p (S36), 12p (S33), 13½p (S34), 14p (S40), 15p (S35), 18p (S44), 22p (S47))	7·50	☐
Presentation Pack (*contains* 10p (S30), 12½p (S38), 16p (S42), 20½p (S46), 26p (S49), 28p (S50))	8·00	☐
Presentation Pack (*contains* 10p (S30), 13p (S39), 16p (S42), 17p (S43), 22p (S48), 26p (S49), 28p (S50), 31p (S51))	11·00	☐
Presentation Pack (*contains* 12p (S52), 13p (S53), 17p (S57), 18p (S59), 22p (S65), 26p (S72), 28p (S74), 31p (S76))	8·00	☐

Nos. S55, S61, S63, S68 and S71 come from booklets.
For combined packs containing values from all three Regions see under Northern Ireland.

1993 (7 DEC)-**97** *Perf 15 × 14 (with one elliptical hole on each vertical side)*

(a) Printed in lithography by Questa

S81	S 4	19p bistre (1 centre band)	40	40	☐	☐
S82		19p bistre (1 side band)	2·25	2·25	☐	☐
S83		20p brt green (1 centre band)	30	35	☐	☐
S84		25p red (2 bands)	50	50	☐	☐
S85		26p red-brn (2 bands)	40	45	☐	☐
S86		30p deep olive-grey (2 bands)	60	60	☐	☐
S87		37p bright mauve (2 bands)	60	65	☐	☐
S88		41p grey-brown (2 bands)	90	90	☐	☐
S89		63p light emerald (2 bands)	95	1·00	☐	☐

(b) Printed in photogravure by Walsall (20p, 63p), Harrison or Walsall (26p, 37p).

S90	S 4	20p bright green (1 centre band)	30	35	☐	☐
S91		26p chestnut (2 bands)	40	45	☐	☐
S92		37p bright mauve (2 bands)	60	65	☐	☐
S93		63p light emerald (2 bands)	95	1·00	☐	☐

No. S82 was only issued in booklets.
For combined presentation packs for all three Regions, see under Northern Ireland.

3 Wales and Monmouthshire

W 1   W 2   W 3

1958–67

W1	W 1	3d lilac	20	10
		p One centre phosphor band	20	15
W2		4d blue	20	15
		p Two phosphor bands	20	15
W3	W 2	6d purple	40	20
W4		9d bronze-green (2 phosphor bands)	40	40
W5	W 3	1s 3d green	30	30
W6		1s 6d blue (2 phosphor bands)	35	40

1967–69 One centre phosphor band (Nos. W7, W9/10) or two phosphor bands (others). No wmk

W7	W 1	3d lilac	20	10	☐	☐
W8		4d blue	20	10	☐	☐
W9		4d sepia	20	10	☐	☐
W10		4d vermilion	20	20	☐	☐
W11		5d blue	20	10	☐	☐
W12	W 3	1s 6d blue	3·00	3·75	☐	☐
		Presentation Pack (comprises Nos. W4, W6/7, W9/11)	3·75		☐	

W 4 With "p"   W 5 Without "p"

Decimal Currency

1971–92 Type W 4. No wmk

(a) Printed in photogravure with phosphor bands

W13	2½p magenta (1 centre band)	20	15	☐	☐
W14	3p ultramarine (2 bands)	25	15	☐	☐
W15	3p ultramarine (1 centre band)	20	20	☐	☐
W16	3½p olive-grey (2 bands)	20	25	☐	☐
W17	3½p olive-grey (1 centre band)	20	25	☐	☐
W18	4½p grey-blue (2 bands)	25	20	☐	☐
W19	5p violet (2 bands)	1·00	1·00	☐	☐
W20	5½p violet (2 bands)	20	25	☐	☐
W21	5½p violet (1 centre band)	20	25	☐	☐
W22	6½p blue (1 centre band)	20	20	☐	☐
W23	7p brown (1 centre band)	25	25	☐	☐
W24	7½p chestnut (2 bands)	1·25	1·50	☐	☐
W25	8p rosine (2 bands)	30	30	☐	☐
W26	8½p yellow-green (2 bands)	30	30	☐	☐
W27	9p violet (2 bands)	30	30	☐	☐
W28	10p orange-brown (2 bands)	35	30	☐	☐
W29	10p orange-brown (1 centre band)	35	30	☐	☐
W30	10½p blue (2 bands)	50	50	☐	☐
W31	11p scarlet (2 bands)	50	50	☐	☐

(b) Printed in photogravure on phosphorised paper

W32	12p yellow-green	50	45	☐	☐
W33	13½p purple-brown	60	70	☐	☐
W34	15p ultramarine	60	50	☐	☐

(c) Printed in lithography. Perf 14 (11½p, 12½p, 14p (No. W39), 15½p, 16p, 18p (No. W46), 19½p, 20½p, 22p (No. W54), 26p (No. W61), 28p (No. W63)) or 15 × 14 (others).

W35	11½p drab (1 side band)	85	60	☐	☐
W36	12p brt emer (1 side band)	1·25	1·10	☐	☐
W37	12½p light emer (1 side band)	80	60	☐	☐
	a. Perf 15 × 14	6·00	6·00	☐	☐
W38	13p pale chest (1 side band)	50	35	☐	☐
W39	14p grey-blue (phosphorised paper)	65	50	☐	☐
W40	14p dp blue (1 centre band)	55	50	☐	☐
W41	15p brt blue (1 centre band)	50	50	☐	☐
W42	15½p pale violet (phosphorised paper)	80	65	☐	☐
W43	16p drab (phosphorised paper)	1·75	1·25	☐	☐
	a. Perf 15 × 14	1·75	1·50	☐	☐
W44	17p grey-blue (phosphorised paper)	90	70	☐	☐
W45	17p deep blue (1 centre band)	70	55	☐	☐
W46	18p deep violet (phosphorised paper)	80	75	☐	☐
W47	18p olive-grey (phosphorised paper)	80	70	☐	☐
W48	18p brt grn (1 centre band)	55	55	☐	☐
	b. Perf 14	1·25	1·00	☐	☐
W49	18p brt green (1 side band)	2·00	2·00	☐	☐
W50	19p bright orange-red (phosphorised paper)	85	60	☐	☐
W51	19½p olive-grey (phosphorised paper)	2·00	2·00	☐	☐
W52	20p brownish black (phosphorised paper)	80	80	☐	☐
W53	20½p ultramarine (phosphorised paper)	4·00	4·00	☐	☐
W54	22p blue (phosphorised paper)	1·10	1·10	☐	☐
W55	22p yell-green (phosphorised paper)	90	1·25	☐	☐
W56	22p bright orange-red (phosphorised paper)	80	70	☐	☐

W57	23p brt green (phosphorised paper)	90	1·25	□	□
W58	24p Indian red (phosphorised paper)	1·00	1·25	□	□
W59	24p chestnut (phosphorised paper)	90	90	□	□
	b. Perf 14	1·40	1·00	□	□
W60	24p chestnut (2 bands)	1·10	1·10	□	□
W61	26p rosine (phosphorised paper)	1·10	1·40	□	□
	a. Perf 15 × 14	4·75	5·00	□	□
W62	26p drab (phosphorised paper)	1·00	1·00	□	□
W63	28p dp viol-blue (phosphorised paper)	1·10	1·25	□	□
	a. Perf 15 × 14	1·10	1·10	□	□
W64	28p deep bluish grey (phosphorised paper)	1·10	1·10	□	□
W65	31p brt purple (phosphorised paper)	1·25	1·25	□	□
W66	32p greenish blue (phosphorised paper)	1·25	1·25	□	□
W67	34p deep bluish grey (phosphorised paper)	1·10	1·40	□	□
W68	37p rosine (phosphorised paper)	1·10	1·40	□	□
W69	39p bright mauve (phosphorised paper)	1·10	1·40	□	□

Presentation Pack (contains 2½p (W13), 3p (W14), 5p (W19), 7½p (W24)) — 4·25 □

Presentation Pack (contains 3p (W15), 3½p (W16), 5½p (W20), 8p (W25), later with 4½p (W18) added) — 2·50 □

Presentation Pack (contains 6½p (W22), 8½p (W26), 10p (W28), 11p (W31)) — 2·00 □

Presentation Pack (contains 7p (W23), 9p (W27), 10½p (W30), 11½p (W35), 12p (W32), 13½p (W33), 14p (W39), 15p (W34), 18p (W46), 22p (W53)) — 7·50 □

Presentation Pack (contains 10p (W29), 12½p (W37), 16p (W43), 20½p (W53), 26p (W61), 28p (W63)) — 8·00 □

Presentation Pack (contains 10p (W29), 13p (W38), 16p (W43a), 17p (W44), 22p (W55), 26p (W61), 28p (W63), 31p (W65)) — 11·00 □

Presentation Pack (contains 12p (W36), 13p (W38), 17p (W44), 18p (W47), 22p (W55), 26p (W61a), 28p (W63a), 31p (W65)) — 10·00 □

Nos. W49 and W60 come from booklets. The former ex with the phosphor band at the left or the right of the star

For combined packs containing values from all th Regions see under Northern Ireland.

1993 (7 Dec.)-**96** Printed in lithography by Questa. F 15 × 14 (with one elliptical hole on each vertical side)

W70	W 4	19p bistre (1 centre band)	40	40	□
W71		19p bistre (1 side band)	2·25	2·25	□
W72		20p brt green (1 centre band)	30	35	□
W73		25p red (2 bands)	50	50	□
W74		26p red-brn (2 bands)	40	45	□
W75		30p deep olive-grey (2 bands)	60	60	□
W76		37p bright mauve (2 bands)	60	65	□
W77		41p grey-brown (2 bands)	90	90	□
W78		63p light emerald (2 bands)	95	1·00	□

No. W71 was only issued in booklets.

For combined presentation packs for all three Regions under Northern Ireland.

1997 (1 July). Printed in photogravure by Walsall (20p, 63 Harrison or Walsall (26p, 37p). Perf 15 × 14 (with elliptical hole on each vertical side)

W79	W 5	20p bright green (1 centre band)	30	35	□
W80		26p chestnut (2 bands)	40	45	□
W81		37p bright mauve (2 bands)	60	65	□
W82		63p light emerald (2 bands)	95	1·00	□
	Presentation Pack		2·75		□

ISLE OF MAN

Regional Issues

1   2   3

1958–67 *Wmk* **179** *Perf* 15 × 14

1	1	2½d red		55	90	☐ ☐
2	2	3d lilac		20	10	☐ ☐
		p. *One centre phosphor band*		20	40	☐ ☐
3		4d blue		1·60	1·25	☐ ☐
		p. *Two phosphor bands*		20	25	☐ ☐

1968–69 *One centre phosphor band (Nos. 5/6) or two phosphor bands (others). No wmk*

4	2	4d blue		20	25	☐ ☐
5		4d sepia		20	30	☐ ☐
6		4d vermilion		50	70	☐ ☐
7		5d blue		50	70	☐ ☐

Decimal Currency

1971 (7 July) *One centre phosphor band (2½p) or two phosphor bands (others). No wmk*

8	3	2½p magenta		20	15	☐ ☐
9		3p ultramarine		20	15	☐ ☐
10		5p violet		50	60	☐ ☐
11		7½p chestnut		50	75	☐ ☐
		Presentation Pack		2·00		☐

For comprehensive listings of the Independent Administration issues of the Isle of Man, see Stanley Gibbons *Collect Channel Islands and Isle of Man Stamps.*

CHANNEL ISLANDS

1 General Issue

C 1 Gathering Vraic   C 2 Islanders gathering Vraic

Third Anniversary of Liberation

1948 (10 May) *Wmk Type* **127** *Perf* 15 × 14

C1	C 1	1d red		20	20	☐ ☐
C2	C 2	2½d blue		30	30	☐ ☐
		First Day Cover		26·00		☐

---

2 Guernsey

(a) War Occupation Issues

Stamps issued under British authority during the German Occupation.

1   2   3

1941–44 *Rouletted.* (a) *White paper. No wmk*

1f	1	½d green		2·50	2·25	☐ ☐
2		1d red		2·00	1·00	☐ ☐
3		2½d blue		4·00	4·00	☐ ☐

(b) *Bluish French bank-note paper. Wmk loops*

4	1	½d green		18·00	19·00	☐ ☐
5		1d red		9·00	21·00	☐ ☐

(b) Regional Issues

1958–67 *Wmk* **179** *Perf* 15 × 14

6	2	2½d red		35	40	☐ ☐
7	3	3d lilac		35	30	☐ ☐
		p. *One centre phosphor band*		20	20	☐ ☐
8		4d blue		25	30	☐ ☐
		p. *Two phosphor bands*		20	20	☐ ☐

1968–69 *One centre phosphor band (Nos 10/11) or two phosphor bands (others). No wmk*

9	3	4d blue		10	25	☐ ☐
10		4d sepia		15	20	☐ ☐
11		4d vermilion		15	30	☐ ☐
12		5d blue		15	30	☐ ☐

For comprehensive listings of the Independent Postal Administration issues of Guernsey, see Stanley Gibbons *Collect Channel Islands and Isle of Man Stamps.*

3 Jersey

(a) War Occupation Issues

Stamps issued under British authority during the German Occupation.

1   2 Old Jersey Farm   3 Portelet Bay

4 Corbière Lighthouse

5 Elizabeth Castle

6 Mont Orgueil Castle

7 Gathering Vraic (seaweed)

1941–42 *White paper No wmk Perf 11*

1	1	½d green	..	3·75	3·00	☐ ☐
2		1d red	.. ..	4·00	3·00	☐ ☐

1943 *No wmk Perf 13½*

3	2	½d green	..	8·00	7·25	☐ ☐
4	3	1d red	.. ..	2·25	1·00	☐ ☐
5	4	1½d brown	..	4·00	4·00	☐ ☐
6	5	2d orange	..	5·25	4·00	☐ ☐
7a	6	2½d blue	..	1·40	2·25	☐ ☐
8	7	3d violet	..	1·40	3·75	☐ ☐
	Set of 6		.. ..	20·00	20·00	☐ ☐

(b) Regional Issues

8

9

1958–67 *Wmk 179 Perf 15 × 14*

9	8	2½d red	..	35	60	☐ ☐
10	9	3d lilac	..	35	30	☐ ☐
		p One centre phosphor band		20	20	☐ ☐
11		4d blue	..	25	30	☐ ☐
		p Two phosphor bands		20	25	☐ ☐

1968–69 *One centre phosphor band (4d values) or two phosphor bands (5d) No wmk*

12	9	4d sepia	..	20	25	☐ ☐
13		4d vermilion	..	20	35	☐ ☐
14		5d blue	.. ..	20	50	☐ ☐

For comprehensive listings of the Independent Postal Administration issues of Jersey, see Stanley Gibbons *Collect Channel Islands and Isle of Man Stamps*.

REGIONAL FIRST DAY COVERS

PRICES for First Day Covers listed below are for stamps, as indicated, used on illustrated envelopes and postmarked with operational cancellations (before 1964) or with special First Day of Issue cancellations (1964 onwards). First Day postmarks of 8 June 1964 and 7 February 1966 were of the machine cancellation "envelope" type.

£sd Issues

18 Aug. 1958	Guernsey 3d (*No.* 7)	.. ..	17·00 ☐
	Isle of Man 3d (*No.* 2)	..	28·00 ☐
	Jersey 3d (*No.* 10)	.. ..	17·00 ☐
	Northern Ireland 3d (*No.* NI1)	..	28·00 ☐
	Scotland 3d (*No.* S1)	.. ..	11·00 ☐
	Wales 3d (*No.* W1)	.. ..	11·00 ☐
29 Sept. 1958	Northern Ireland 6d, 1s 3d (*Nos.* NI3, NI5)	.. ..	32·00 ☐
	Scotland 6d, 1s 3d (*Nos* S3, S5)	..	22·00 ☐
	Wales 6d, 1s 3d (*Nos.* W3, W5)	..	22·00 ☐
8 June 1964	Guernsey 2½d (*No.* 6)	..	22·00 ☐
	Isle of Man 2½d (*No.* 1)	..	28·00 ☐
	Jersey 2½d (*No.* 9)	.. ..	22·00 ☐
7 Feb. 1966	Guernsey 4d (*No.* 8)	.. ..	7·50 ☐
	Isle of Man 4d (*No.* 3)	..	7·50 ☐
	Jersey 4d (*No.* 11)	.. ..	7·50 ☐
	Northern Ireland 4d (*No.* NI2)	..	7·00 ☐
	Scotland 4d (*No.* S2)	.. ..	7·00 ☐
	Wales 4d (*No.* W2)	.. ..	7·00 ☐
1 March 1967	Northern Ireland 9d, 1s 6d (*Nos.* NI4, NI6)	.. ..	2·50 ☐
	Scotland 9d, 1s 6d (*Nos.* S4, S6)	.. ..	2·50 ☐
	Wales 9d, 1s 6d (*Nos.* W4, W6)	..	2·50 ☐
4 Sept. 1968	Guernsey 4d, 5d (*Nos.* 10, 12)	..	1·75 ☐
	Isle of Man 4d, 5d (*Nos.* 5, 7)	..	2·00 ☐
	Jersey 4d, 5d (*Nos.* 12, 14)	..	1·75 ☐
	Northern Ireland 4d, 5d (*Nos.* NI8, NI10)	.. ..	1·75 ☐
	Scotland 4d, 5d (*Nos.* S9, S11)	..	1·75 ☐
	Wales 4d, 5d (*Nos.* W9, W11)	..	1·75 ☐

Decimal Issues

7 July 1971	Isle of Man 2½p, 3p, 5p, 7½p (*Nos.* 8/11)	..	2·50 ☐
	Northern Ireland 2½p, 3p, 5p, 7½p (*Nos.* NI12/13, NI18, NI23)	..	2·50 ☐
	Scotland 2½p, 3p, 5p, 7½p (*Nos.* S14/15, S20, S25)	.. ..	2·50 ☐
	Wales 2½p, 3p, 5p, 7½p (*Nos.* W13/14, W19, W24)	..	2·50 ☐
23 Jan. 1974	Northern Ireland 3p, 3½p, 5½p, 8p (*Nos.* NI14/15, NI19, NI24)	..	1·50 ☐
	Scotland 3p, 3½p, 5½p, 8p (*Nos.* S16/17, S21, S26)	.. ..	1·50 ☐
	Wales 3p, 3½p, 5½p, 8p (*Nos.* W15/16, W20, W25)	.. ..	1·50 ☐

6 Nov. 1974	*Northern Ireland* 4½p, (*No.* NI17)	1·25 ☐
	Scotland 4½p (*No.* S19)	1·25 ☐
	Wales 4½p (*No.* W18)	1·25 ☐
14 Jan. 1976	*Northern Ireland* 6½p, 8½p (*Nos.* NI21, NI25)	1·25 ☐
	Scotland 6½p, 8½p (*Nos.* S23, S27)	1·25 ☐
	Wales 6½p, 8½p (*Nos.* W22, W26)	1·25 ☐
20 Oct. 1976	*Northern Ireland* 10p, 11p (*Nos.* NI27, NI30)	1·25 ☐
	Scotland 10p, 11p (*Nos.* S29, S32)	1·25 ☐
	Wales 10p, 11p (*Nos.* W28, W31)	1·25 ☐
18 Jan. 1978	*Northern Ireland* 7p, 9p, 10½p (*Nos.* NI22, NI26, NI29)	2·00 ☐
	Scotland 7p, 9p, 10½p (*Nos.* S24, S28, S31)	2·00 ☐
	Wales 7p, 9p, 10½p (*Nos.* W23, W27, W30)	2·00 ☐
23 July 1980	*Northern Ireland* 12p, 13½p, 15p (*Nos.* NI31/3)	2·25 ☐
	Scotland 12p, 13½p, 15p (*Nos.* S33/5)	2·25 ☐
	Wales 12p, 13½p, 15p (*Nos.* W32/4)	2·25 ☐
8 April 1981	*Northern Ireland* 11½p, 14p, 18p, 22p (Nos. NI34, NI38, NI45, NI53)	2·25 ☐
	Scotland 11½p, 14p, 18p, 22p (Nos. S36, S40, S44, S47)	2·25 ☐
	Wales 11½p, 14p, 18p, 22p (*Nos.* W35, W39, W46, W54)	2·25 ☐
24 Feb. 1982	*Northern Ireland* 12½p, 15½p, 19½p, 26p (*Nos.* NI36, NI41, NI50, NI60)	2·50 ☐
	Scotland 12½p, 15½p, 19½p, 26p (*Nos.* S38, S41, S45, S49)	2·50 ☐
	Wales 12½p, 15½p, 19½p, 26p (*Nos.* W37, W42, W51, W61)	2·50 ☐
27 April 1983	*Northern Ireland* 16p, 20½p, 28p (*Nos.* NI42, NI52, NI62)	2·75 ☐
	Scotland 16p, 20½p, 28p (*Nos.* S42, S46, S50)	2·75 ☐
	Wales 16p, 20½p, 28p (*Nos.* W43, W53, W63)	6·00 ☐
23 Oct. 1984	*Northern Ireland* 13p, 17p, 22p, 31p (*Nos.* NI37, NI43, NI54, NI64)	2·50 ☐
	Scotland 13p, 17p, 22p, 31p (*Nos.* S39, S43, S48, S51)	2·50 ☐
	Wales 13p, 17p, 22p, 31p (*Nos.* W38, W44, W55, W65)	2·75 ☐

7 Jan. 1986	*Northern Ireland* 12p (*No.* NI35)	1·50 ☐
	Scotland 12p (*No.* S37)	1·50 ☐
	Wales 12p (*No.* W36)	1·50 ☐
6 Jan. 1987	*Northern Ireland* 18p (*No.* NI46)	1·50 ☐
	Scotland 18p (*No.* S59)	1·50 ☐
	Wales 18p (*No.* W47)	1·50 ☐
8 Nov. 1988	*Northern Ireland* 14p, 19p, 23p, 32p (*Nos.* NI39, NI49, NI56, NI65)	2·25 ☐
	Scotland 14p, 19p, 23p, 32p (*Nos.* S54, S62, S67, S77)	2·25 ☐
	Wales 14p, 19p, 23p, 32p (*Nos.* W40, W50, W57, W66)	2·25 ☐
28 Nov. 1989	*Northern Ireland* 15p, 20p, 24p, 34p (*Nos.* NI40, NI51, NI57, NI66)	2·50 ☐
	Scotland 15p, 20p, 24p, 34p (*Nos.* S56, S64, S69, S78)	2·50 ☐
	Wales 15p, 20p, 24p, 34p (*Nos.* W41, W52, W58, W67)	2·50 ☐
4 Dec. 1990	*Northern Ireland* 17p, 22p, 26p, 37p (*Nos.* NI44, NI55, NI61, NI67)	3·25 ☐
	Scotland 17p, 22p, 26p, 37p (*Nos.* S58, S66, S73, S79)	3·25 ☐
	Wales 17p, 22p, 26p, 37p (*Nos.* W45, W56, W62, W68)	3·25 ☐
3 Dec. 1991	*Northern Ireland* 18p, 24p, 28p, 39p (*Nos.* NI47, NI58, NI63, NI68)	3·25 ☐
	Scotland 18p, 24p, 28p, 39p (*Nos.* S60, S70, S75, S80)	3·25 ☐
	Wales 18p, 24p, 28p, 39p (*Nos.* W48, W59, W64, W69)	3·25 ☐
7 Dec. 1993	*Northern Ireland* 19p, 25p, 30p, 41p (*Nos.* NI69, NI72, NI74, NI76)	4·50 ☐
	Scotland 19p, 25p, 30p, 41p (*Nos.* S81, S84, S86, S88)	4·50 ☐
	Wales 19p, 25p, 30p, 41p (*Nos.* W70, W73, W75, W77)	4·50 ☐
23 July 1996	*Northern Ireland* 20p, 26p, 37p, 63p (*Nos.* NI71, NI73, NI75, NI77)	3·25 ☐
	Scotland 20p, 26p, 37p, 63p (*Nos.* S83, S85, S87, S89)	3·25 ☐
	Wales 20p, 26p, 37p, 63p (*Nos.* W72, W74, W76, W78)	3·25 ☐
1 July 1997	*Wales* 20p, 26p, 37p, 63p, (*Nos.* W79/82)	3·25 ☐

POSTAGE DUE STAMPS

PERFORATION. All postage due stamps are perf 14 × 1$\frac{1}{2}$

D 1   D 2

1914–22 *Wmk Type* **96** (*Royal Cypher* (*'Simple'*)) *sideway*

D1	D 1	$\frac{1}{2}$d green	..	..	50	50 ☐
D2		1d red	..	..	50	50 ☐
D3		1$\frac{1}{2}$d brown	..	..	40·00	18·00 ☐
D4		2d black	..	..	50	70 ☐
D5		3d violet	..	..	2·50	1·00 ☐
D6		4d green	..	..	25·00	4·00 ☐
D7		5d brown	..	..	5·00	3·25 ☐
D8		1s blue	..	..	28·00	3·75 ☐
	Set of 8 ..		..	..	90·00	28·00 ☐

1924–31 *Wmk Type* **107** (*Block* G v R) *sideways*

D10	D 1	$\frac{1}{2}$d green	..	..	90	75 ☐
D11		1d red	..	..	60	60 ☐
D12		1$\frac{1}{2}$d brown	..	..	40·00	18·00 ☐
D13		2d black	..	..	1·00	40 ☐
D14		3d violet	..	..	1·50	40 ☐
D15		4d green	..	..	13·00	3·00 ☐
D16		5d brown	..	..	29·00	22·00 ☐
D17		1s blue	..	..	8·50	75 ☐
D18	D 2	2s 6d purple/*yellow*	..		40·00	2·00 ☐
	Set of 9 ..		..	..	£120	45·00 ☐

1936–37 *Wmk Type* **125** (E 8 R) *sideways*

D19	D 1	$\frac{1}{2}$d green	..	..	7·50	7·00 ☐
D20		1d red	..	..	1·50	1·50 ☐
D21		2d black	..	..	7·00	9·00 ☐
D22		3d violet	..	..	1·50	1·60 ☐
D23		4d green	..	..	23·00	23·00 ☐
D24a		5d brown	..	..	16·00	21·00 ☐
D25		1s blue	..	..	11·00	7·00 ☐
D26	D 2	2s 6d purple/*yellow*	..		£250	8·00 ☐
	Set of 8 ..		..	..	£300	70·00 ☐

1937–38 *Wmk Type* **127** (G vi R) *sideways*

D27	D 1	$\frac{1}{2}$d green	..	..	8·00	4·50 ☐
D28		1d red	..	..	2·50	50 ☐
D29		2d black	..	..	2·50	50 ☐
D30		3d violet	..	..	12·00	90 ☐
D31		4d green	..	..	65·00	10·00 ☐
D32		5d brown	..	..	12·00	1·50 ☐
D33		1s blue	..	..	60·00	1·50 ☐
D34	D 2	2s 6d purple/*yellow*	..		60·00	2·50 ☐
	Set of 8 ..		..	..	£200	19·00 ☐

1951–52 *Colours changed and new value* (1$\frac{1}{2}$d) *Wmk Typ*
127 (G vi R) *sideways*

D35	D 1	$\frac{1}{2}$d orange	..	..	1·00	2·50 ☐
D36		1d blue	..	..	1·50	1·25 ☐
D37		1$\frac{1}{2}$d green	..	..	1·75	2·50 ☐
D38		4d blue	..	..	30·00	11·00 ☐
D39		1s brown	..	..	35·00	13·00 ☐
	Set of 5 ..		..	..	60·00	22·00 ☐

954–55 *Wmk Type* **153** (*Mult. Tudor Crown and* E 2 R) *deways*

40	D **1**	½d	orange	6·00	4·50	□	□
41		2d	black	4·00	4·00	□	□
42		3d	violet	50·00	32·00	□	□
43		4d	blue	18·00	19·00	□	□
44		5d	brown	25·00	9·00	□	□
45	D **2**	2s 6d	purple/*yellow*	£100	3·00	□	□
	Set of 6			£190	65·00	□	□

55–57 *Wmk Type* **165** (*Mult. St Edward's Crown and* 2 R) *sideways*

46	D **1**	½d	orange	1·25	2·25	□	□
47		1d	blue	5·50	1·50	□	□
48		1½d	green	5·50	5·00	□	□
49		2d	black	40·00	3·25	□	□
50		3d	violet	6·00	1·25	□	□
51		4d	blue	21·00	3·75	□	□
52		5d	brown	32·00	2·00	□	□
53		1s	brown	70·00	2·00	□	□
54	D **2**	2s 6d	purple/*yellow*	£140	8·00	□	□
55		5s	red/*yellow*	80·00	25·00	□	□
	Set of 10			£350	48·00	□	□

59–63 *Wmk Type* **179** (*Mult. St Edward's Crown*) *deways*

56	D **1**	½d	orange	10	1·00	□	□
57		1d	blue	10	50	□	□
58		1½d	green	90	2·75	□	□
59		2d	black	1·25	50	□	□
60		3d	violet	40	30	□	□
61		4d	blue	40	30	□	□
62		5d	brown	45	75	□	□
63		6d	purple	60	30	□	□
64		1s	brown	1·40	30	□	□
65	D **2**	2s 6d	purple/*yellow*	4·25	45	□	□
66		5s	red/*yellow*	8·00	1·00	□	□
67		10s	blue/*yellow*	10·00	5·00	□	□
68		£1	black/*yellow*	45·00	8·00	□	□
	Set of 13			65·00	19·00	□	□

68–69 *Design size* 22½ × 19 *mm No wmk*

69	D **1**	2d	black	20	60	□	□
70		3d	violet	25	60	□	□
71		4d	blue	25	60	□	□
72		5d	orange-brown	5·00	6·00	□	□
73		6d	purple	60	90	□	□
74		1s	brown	2·00	1·40	□	□
	Set of 6			7·50	9·00	□	□

68–69 *Design size* 21½ × 17½ *mm No wmk*

75	D **1**	4d	blue	5·00	5·00	□	□
76		8d	red	1·00	1·00	□	□

D **4**

Decimal Currency

1970–77 *No wmk*

D77	D **3**	½p	turquoise-blue	10	20	□	□
D78		1p	reddish purple	10	15	□	□
D79		2p	myrtle-green	10	15	□	□
D80		3p	ultramarine	15	15	□	□
D81		4p	yellow-brown	15	15	□	□
D82		5p	violet	20	20	□	□
D83		7p	red-brown	35	45	□	□
D84	D **4**	10p	red	30	20	□	□
D85		11p	green	60	60	□	□
D86		20p	brown	60	50	□	□
D87		50p	ultramarine	1·50	50	□	□
D88		£1	black	3·50	75	□	□
D89		£5	orange-yellow and black	35·00	2·00	□	□
	Set of 13			38·00	5·00	□	□
D77/82, D84, D86/8 *Presentation Pack*				11·00			□
D77/88 *Presentation Pack*				6·00			□

D **5**

D **6**

D **7**

1982 *No wmk*

D 90	D **5**	1p	lake	10	10	□	□
D 91		2p	bright blue	20	10	□	□
D 92		3p	deep mauve	10	15	□	□
D 93		4p	deep blue	10	20	□	□
D 94		5p	sepia	20	20	□	□
D 95	D **6**	10p	light brown	20	25	□	□
D 96		20p	olive-green	40	30	□	□
D 97		25p	deep greenish blue	50	70	□	□
D 98		50p	grey-black	1·00	75	□	□
D 99		£1	red	2·00	50	□	□
D100		£2	turquoise-blue	4·50	50	□	□
D101		£5	dull orange	12·00	50	□	□
	Set of 12			19·00	3·75	□	□
	Set of 12 *Gutter Pairs*			40·00		□	
	Presentation Pack			20·00		□	

1994 (15 Feb.) *Perf* 15 × 14 (*with one elliptical hole on each vertical side*)

D102	D **7**	1p.	red, yellow and black	10	10	□	□
D103		2p.	magenta, purple and black	10	10	□	□
D104		5p.	yellow, red-brown and black	10	10	□	□
D105		10p.	yellow, emerald and black	15	20	□	□

D106	D 7	20p. blue-green, violet and black	30	35	☐ ☐
D107		25p. cerise, rosine and black	40	45	☐ ☐
D108		£1 violet, magenta and black	1·50	1·60	☐ ☐
D109		£1.20 greenish blue, blue-green and black	1·75	1·90	☐ ☐
D110		£5 greenish black, blue-green and black	7·50	7·75	☐ ☐
		Set of 9	11·50	12·50	☐ ☐
		Presentation Pack	12·00		☐

ROYAL MAIL POSTAGE LABELS

These imperforate labels were issued as an experiment by the Post Office. Special microprocessor controlled machines were installed at post offices in Cambridge, London, Shirley (Southampton) and Windsor to provide an after-hours sales service to the public. The machines printed and dispensed the labels according to the coins inserted and the buttons operated by the customer. Values were initially available in $\frac{1}{2}$p steps to 16p and in addition, the labels were sold at philatelic counters in two packs containing either 3 values ($3\frac{1}{2}$, $12\frac{1}{2}$, 16p) or 32 values ($\frac{1}{2}$p to 16p).

From 28 August 1984 the machines were adjusted to provide values up to 17p. After 31 December 1984 labels including $\frac{1}{2}$p values were withdrawn. The machines were taken out of service on 30 April 1985.

Machine postage-paid impression in red on phosphorised paper with grey-green background design. No watermark Imperforate

1984 (1 May – 28 Aug)

Set of 32 ($\frac{1}{2}$p to 16p)	17·00	25·00	☐ ☐
Set of 3 ($3\frac{1}{2}$p, $12\frac{1}{2}$p, 16p)	3·00	3·50	☐ ☐
Set of 3 on First Day Cover (1 May)		6·50	☐
Set of 2 ($16\frac{1}{2}$p, 17p) (28 August)	4·50	4·50	☐ ☐

OFFICIAL STAMPS

Various Stamps of Queen Victoria and King Edward VII Overprinted in Black.

I.R.	I. R.	O. W.
OFFICIAL	**OFFICIAL**	OFFICIAL
(O 1)	(O 2)	(O 3)

ARMY		
	ARMY	**GOV\u1d40**
OFFICIAL	**OFFICIAL**	**PARCELS**
(O 4)	(O 5)	(O 7)

BOARD	**R.H.**	**ADMIRALTY**
OF		
EDUCATION	**OFFICIAL**	**OFFICIAL**
(O 8)	(O 9)	(O 10)

1 Inland Revenue

Overprinted with Types O 1 or O 2 (5s, 10s, £1)

1882–1901 *Queen Victoria*

O 1	52	$\frac{1}{2}$d	green	12·00	3·00	☐ ☐
O 5		$\frac{1}{2}$d	blue	25·00	15·00	☐ ☐
O13	67	$\frac{1}{2}$d	vermilion	1·50	50	☐ ☐
O17		·d	green	4·00	3·00	☐ ☐
O 3	57	1d	lilac (Die II)	1·50	65	☐ ☐
O 6	64	$2\frac{1}{2}$d	lilac	£120	40·00	☐ ☐
O14	70	$2\frac{1}{2}$d	purple on blue	50·00	4·00	☐ ☐
O 4	43	6d	grey (Plate 18)	75·00	20·00	☐ ☐
O18	75	6d	purple on red	£100	22·00	☐ ☐
O 7	65	1s	green	£2500	£450	☐ ☐
O15	78	1s	green	£225	25·00	☐ ☐
O19		1s	green and red	£800	£175	☐ ☐
O 9	59	5s	red	£1300	£400	☐ ☐
O10	60	10s	blue	£2500	£525	☐ ☐
·O11	61	£1	brown (Wmk Crowns)	£20000		☐ ☐
O12		£1	brown (Wmk Orbs)	£27500		☐ ☐
O16		£1	green	£3750	£500	☐ ☐

O20	79	½d	blue-green	17·00	1·50	□	□
O21		1d	red	10·00	70	□	□
O22	82	2½d	blue	£450	90·00	□	□
O23	79	6d	purple	£85000	£65000	□	□
O24	89	1s	green and red	£550	95·00	□	□
O25	91	5s	red	£4000	£1500	□	□
O26	92	10s	blue	£15000	£9500	□	□
O27	93	£1	green	£12000	£7000	□	□

2 Office of Works

Overprinted with Type O 3

1896–1902 *Queen Victoria*

O31	67	½d	vermilion	90·00	40·00	□	□
O32		½d	green	£150	75·00	□	□
O33	57	1d	lilac (Die II)	£150	40·00	□	□
O34	74	5d	dull pur & bl	£800	£175	□	□
O35	77	10d	dull pur & red	£1400	£275	□	□

1902–03 *King Edward VII*

O36	79	½d	blue-green	£350	80·00	□	□
O37		1d	red	£350	80·00	□	□
O38	81	2d	green and red	£600	80·00	□	□
O39	82	2½d	blue	£700	£250	□	□
O40	88	10d	purple and red	£5000	£1500	□	□

3 Army

Overprinted with Types O 4 (½d, 1d) or O 5 (2½d, 6d)

1896–1901 *Queen Victoria*

O41	67	½d	vermilion	1·50	75	□	□
O42		½d	green	1·75	4·00	□	□
O43	57	1d	lilac (Die II)	1·50	75	□	□
O44	70	2½d	purple on blue	4·00	3·00	□	□
O45	75	6d	purple on red	16·00	10·00	□	□

Overprinted with Type O 4

1902 *King Edward VII*

O48	79	½d	blue-green	2·00	65	□	□
O49		1d	red	1·50	55	□	□
O50		6d	purple	70·00	32·00	□	□

4 Government Parcels

Overprinted with Type O 7

1883–1900 *Queen Victoria*

O69	57	1d	lilac (Die II)	28·00	8·00	□	□
O61	62	1½d	lilac	£100	25·00	□	□
O65	68	1½d	purple and green	14·00	2·00	□	□
O70	69	2d	green and red	45·00	7·00	□	□
O71	73	4½d	green and red	£100	75·00	□	□
O62	63	6d	green	£800	£275	□	□
O66	75	6d	purple on red	28·00	10·00	□	□
O63	64	9d	green	£650	£180	□	□
O67	76	9d	purple and blue	55·00	15·00	□	□
O64	44	1s	brown (Plate 13)	£425	70·00	□	□
O64c		1s	brown (Plate 14)	£750	£110	□	□
O68	78	1s	green	£120	70·00	□	□
O72		1s	green and red	£160	50·00	□	□

1902 *King Edward VII*

O74	79	1d	red	17·00	6·00	□	□
O75	81	2d	green and red	65·00	18·00	□	□
O76	79	6d	purple	£100	18·00	□	□
O77	87	9d	purple and blue	£225	50·00	□	□
O78	89	1s	green and red	£350	85·00	□	□

5 Board of Education

Overprinted with Type O 8

1902 *Queen Victoria*

O81	74	5d	dull pur & bl	£575	£120	□	□
O82	78	1s	green and red	£1000	£400	□	□

1902–04 *King Edward VII*

O83	79	½d	blue-green	20·00	8·00	□	□
O84		1d	red	20·00	7·00	□	□
O85	82	2½d	blue	£550	60·00	□	□
O86	85	5d	purple and blue	£2250	£1000	□	□
O87	89	1s	green and red	£40000	£30000	□	□

6 Royal Household

Overprinted with Type O 9

1902 *King Edward VII*

O91	79	½d	blue-green	£150	95·00	□	□
O92		1d	red	£130	85·00	□	□

7 Admiralty

Overprinted with Type O 10

1903 *King Edward VII*

O107	79	½d	blue-green	9·00	5·00	□	□
O102		1d	red	5·00	2·50	□	□
O103	80	1½d	purple and green	60·00	45·00	□	□
O104	81	2d	green and red	£110	55·00	□	□
O105	82	2½d	blue	£130	45·00	□	□
O106	83	3d	purple on yellow	£110	40·00	□	□

Minimum Price. The minimum price quoted is 10p. This represents a handling charge rather than a basis for valuing common stamps. Where the actual value of a stamp is less than 10p this may be apparent when set prices are shown, particularly for sets including a number of 10p stamps. It therefore follows that in valuing common stamps the 10p catalogue price should not be reckoned automatically since it covers a variation in real scarcity.

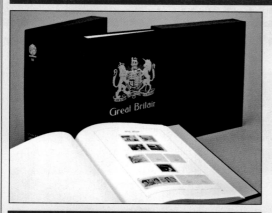

PRINZ STAMP MOUNTS

UNSURPASSED CLARITY & QUALITY - PLUS GUARANTEED SAFETY

PRINZ STANDARD MOUNTS (top opening)

BLACK OR CLEAR BACK
◀ IN TWO STYLES ▶

The back of each mount is coated with extra strength gum, requiring only the lightest of moistening.

PRINZ GARD MOUNTS (back opening)

The world renowned **PRINZ MOUNTS** are available ready cut-to-size for popular G.B. sizes, or in strips/blocks for cutting yourself. All Prinz mounts have reinforced top foil for superior hold

TICK BOX ✔	BLACK BACK	CLEAR BACK	TICK BOX ✔	PRINZ STAND.	PRINZ GARD	ORDER HERE	
						Qty	£ p
25 READY-CUT MOUNTS for G.B. stamp sizes (width x height)							
21 x 24mm	GB definitives			75p	80p		
41 x 24mm	Old commems (horiz)			75p	80p		
24 x 41mm	Old commems (vert)			75p	80p		
41 x 30mm	Commems (horiz) 1967+			75p	80p		
30 x 41mm	Commems (vert) 1967+			75p	80p		
35 x 35mm	Square commems 1984			75p	80p		
37 x 35mm	Oblong (horiz) Comms. 1985+			75p	80p		
35 x 37mm	Oblong (vert) Comms. (1986)			75p	80p		
75 x 41mm	GB Gutter Pairs				£2.00		

25 STRIPS 215mm (8.5ins) long for stamp heights shown			
21mm	GB postage dues, etc.	£3.50	£3.95
24mm	GB definitives, commems	£3.50	£3.95
26mm	USA, Canada commems	£3.50	£3.95
27.5mm	GB Wilding high values	£3.50	£3.95
29mm	Jersey & Guernsey, etc	£3.50	£3.95
30mm	GB commems (horiz)	£3.50	£3.95
31mm	Jersey high values	£3.50	£3.95
33mm	CA Silver Jubilee issues	£3.50	£3.95

36mm	'69-'79 Machin high values	£4.45	£4.95
39mm	PUC £1, various foreign	£4.45	£4.95
41mm	GB commems (vert)	£4.45	£4.95
44mm	Various foreign	£4.45	£4.95
48mm	Battle of Britain, etc.	£4.45	£4.95
49mm	CA Silver Jubilee	£4.45	£4.95
52mm	USA blocks of 4, etc	£4.45	£4.95
55mm	Wilding blocks, etc	£4.45	£4.95

Sub Total c/fd £

? HAVE YOU TICKED BOXES AT LEFT TO SHOW EXACTLY WHICH TYPE OF MOUNT YOU REQUIRE?		ORDER HERE	
		Qty	£ p
STRIP ASSORTMENT PACKS			
200 gms wt. KILOWARE mixed strip sizes	£13.75		
Trial assort (18 strips of mixed sizes)	£3.50	£3.95	

10 STRIPS 215mm (8.5ins) long for stamp heights. shown			
60mm	GB commems, blks four		£3.95
66mm	Larger blocks, etc	£3.50	£3.95
70mm	Machin high values, blks 4		£3.95
75mm	G.B. Gutter blocks		£3.95
86mm	Larger blocks, etc	£3.50	£3.95
92mm	GB miniature		£3.95
100mm	GB cyl blks of 6, etc		£3.95

FOR BLOCKS, F.D.C'S of the max. sizes shown (width x height)			
130 x 85mm	(10 blocks per pkt)	£3.50	£3.95
148 x 105mm	(10 blocks per pkt)	£3.50	£3.95
160 x 120mm	(10 blocks per pkt)	£3.50	£3.95
210 x 170mm	(5 blocks per pkt)	£3.50	£3.95
216 x 115mm	(10) GPO FDC & Pres. Packs		£4.95
Block Assortment Pack: 10 assorted sizes		£3.50	£3.95

CUTTERS: Self sharpening stainless steel blades			
For perfectly cut mounts everytime	G1 Cuts maximum size 100x86mm	£11.50	
	G4 Cuts maximum size 200x170mm	£18.50	

PRICE INCLUDE UK VAT	TOTAL THIS COLUMN £	
OUTSIDE E.E.C. DEDUCT 15%	TOT. PREVIOUS COL £	
ALL O'SEAS: ADD 10% POST & PACKING	GRAND TOTAL	£

UK POST FREE OVER £10 (Under £10 add £1)
IMMEDIATE DESPATCH

Please send me by return the items ordered, and debit my Amex/Mastercard/Visa Account

Date card expires

Signature:

Name:

Address:

Postcode:

Telephone No:

Send today for our full colour album and accessory lists and details of our SPECIAL introductory offers

WEST CORNWALL STAMP CENTRE
13 FORE STREET, HAYLE, CORNWALL TR27 4DX
TEL: 01736 754604 FAX: 01736 756555

Proprietors: Prinz Publications (UK) Ltd.